Virgin Wives

Virgin Wives

A Study of Unconsummated Marriages

LEONARD J. FRIEDMAN
M.D.

Foreword by
MICHAEL BALINT
M.D., PH.D., M.SC.

TAVISTOCK PUBLICATIONS

First published in 1962
in the 'Mind & Medicine Monographs' series
Editor: Michael Balint, M.D., Ph.D., M.Sc.
by Tavistock Publications Limited
11 New Fetter Lane, London E.C.4
SBN 422 70280 3
First published as a Social Science Paperback in 1971
SBN 422 75190 1
Printed in Great Britain
in 11 point Times Roman by
C. Tinling & Co. Ltd, Liverpool, London and Prescot

This paperback edition is distributed
in the U.S.A. by Barnes & Noble, Inc.
A hardback library edition is
distributed in the U.S.A. and Canada
by J. B. Lippincott Company, Philadelphia
and Toronto

CONTENTS

FOREWORD

In 1958 the Family Planning Association initiated a training-cum-research scheme for doctors who were working in their Special Clinics for Marital Problems. A group of ten doctors was formed, and I was asked to work with them. During the three years of our collaboration several problems were studied, and this book is the report on one such. We chose the topic of unconsummated marriages because we thought that —since in most of the cases the therapeutic work had been rather short—the task of writing it up would not be too difficult.

We were greatly surprised to find that, contrary to our expectation, the task proved to be difficult for reasons that should have been apparent to us. A brief reflection will reveal that there must be present high intensities of horror and hatred, disgust, fear, and despair, to prevent the union of husband and wife, which had appeared so desirable to both of them a short time before. As it happened, during the three years of our work we had developed a dispassionate, although certainly not unsympathetic, attitude towards these highly charged problems and we had learnt to accept and work with them, and even to talk about them, both with our patients and among ourselves in our case seminars. The familiarity acquired in this way made us forget the great difference between words spoken and words printed. Thus our first concern was the accuracy of the reporting and not its emotional impact on the reader.

When, therefore, we first asked our colleague, Dr. Leonard Friedman, to write a book about our research, we were unanimous that our work should be presented without attenuation, embellishment, or moralizing. In order to safeguard these standards it was agreed that each case report should be submitted for their approval to the doctors who treated the patients, and each chapter to the whole research team for a thorough discussion.

Thus it happened that while we were taking the greatest care that the work should be truthfully reported, we completely overlooked another important factor—the impact that our material would make on the reader. No one, not even doctors for whose use this book is primarily intended, can avoid responding to some extent emotionally to a report about most intimate human emotions and most intimate forms of human behaviour. Though we can claim that the material presented here gives a truthful account of our work and findings, we are far from confident that we have succeeded in creating the atmosphere of dispassionate sympathy in the reader that is necessary for the study of these most intricate and delicate human problems.

We were very lucky to secure Dr. Friedman's interest in this work. It was his idea to illustrate certain aspects of our findings by similar material from folk-lore and mythology, for he thought that the impact of our experiences on the reader might be made in this way less startling and more tolerable.

We would state explicitly our claim that our diagnostic and therapeutic work with these patients was truly psychosomatic in the strictest sense of the word. The classical gynaecological examination permits the doctor to examine not only the anatomical condition of the female genital organs, but also, to a considerable extent, their physiological or pathological functioning. Our method—as will be seen in this book—was

to integrate into a single performance these two examinations
with a third—a thorough psychological examination of the
woman's emotions and fantasies centred on her genital
organs and their functions. One reason why in our work this
could be done fairly easily was that all the doctors as well
as the patients were women.

At this point it should perhaps be mentioned that we are
fully aware that our research work has studied one side only
of the complex problem of non-consummation. Our experiences have taught us something about the woman's contribution to this impasse. This does not mean that we think
the man's contribution is unimportant; only that our setting
did not enable us to study it. In any case it would be difficult
to create conditions for a proper psychosomatic diagnosis
and therapy for the male partner's problem. We do not know
of any accepted examination that would supply the doctor
with reliable data about the physiological or pathological
functioning of the male sexual organs, and the emotions and
fantasies of the man centred on them, in the way that a
gynaecological examination does in the case of the female.
In the same way, we cannot be certain what influence the sex
of the examining doctor may have on the data obtained. We
thought it advisable to state these impressive differences
clearly in order to put our limited contributions to this vast
problem in the right perspective.

Having stated this, we still wish to stress one surprising
finding of our research. This concerns the immense power
that a number of these women apparently exert over their
menfolk. True, often enough this power is hidden behind an
impressive façade of sweetness and fear, weakness and
despair; nevertheless, it is there. This does not mean that we
think that all women are powerful and dominant. What we
would state is that in the field of unconsummated marriages
power and domination play a very important part. During

the three years of our research work we have already begun to study other groups of women with different problems, among them those complaining of chronic frigidity, of illegitimate pregnancy, and those coming—apparently without any complaint—for premarital advice. As yet we know very little about them, but it is already certain that their world is utterly different from that of the virgin wives, and any work with them will have to be designed to meet new problems and use different diagnostic and therapeutic methods.

After we had finished the research work, one of our team, Dr. E. Mallinson, discovered what is perhaps the first detailed description of the treatment of an unconsummated marriage. We decided to reprint this clinical report as an appendix to the book. The therapist was St. Columba and the date some time between A.D. 563 and 597, that is, while he lived on Iona. Of course the method employed by him was utterly different from our own, but the details of the relationship between husband and wife, on the one hand, and patient and therapist, on the other, reveal the same features of power and dominance that we and our patients have to contend with in the twentieth century.

MICHAEL BALINT

AUTHOR'S PREFACE

Writing an exposition of other people's work is always a delicate task. The research presented in this monograph was carried out by Dr. Michael Balint and ten doctors associated with the Family Planning Association. During the early autumn of 1960, when I was working at the Tavistock Clinic, London, studying group methods for training general practitioners in psychotherapeutic medicine and techniques of group therapy in use there, Balint invited me to attend his F.P.A. seminar with a view towards writing this book. I attended the seminar as a participant observer for nine months, and was provided with stenographic transcripts of all previous meetings. I drew both on my own experience of the seminar and on the transcripts in preparing this work. A draft of each chapter was circulated to all seminar members for comment. Where differences of opinion appeared, they were explored in discussions. On those few aspects of the work where some divergence of view remained between myself and the seminar doctors, I have clearly indicated both points of view.

Psychotherapy involves an intimate exchange between doctor and patient. Particularly when sexual problems are the reason for treatment, the interchange includes matters not usually discussed in print. The training method in use in the seminar depends upon detailed discussion of interview material. For an exposition of this technique to be of value to doctors and other professional workers, some reporting of vivid clinical material is necessary, altered as little as possible from its original form.

In selecting this material for presentation, the need to protect the patient's right to privacy was paramount. All external details about the patient that could conceivably lead to recognition by family or friends were eliminated or changed, and of course false names were used throughout. The doctor who treated the patient in question co-operated in this policy of disguising the material for the patient's protection. Despite these efforts, it is possible that some patient who chances to read this book may recognize herself. Should this unfortunate eventuality occur, we sincerely regret any pain that may be caused to the patient. I hope that she will understand that if this unlikely event occurs, only she will know of it. Any method of presentation that absolutely precluded the possibility of the patient's recognizing herself would falsify the data to such an extent as to render them useless for scientific reporting. The communication to other professional workers of what has been learned from this study will, I hope, benefit other patients who suffer from this difficulty.

I wish to express my gratitude to the Harvard Medical School, not only for granting me the Moseley Travelling Fellowship in Psychiatry, which made my participation in this work possible, but also for the skilled teaching that awakened my interest in psychological medicine as a medical student at the start of my clinical work.

In addition to discussions of the draft manuscript with Balint and the doctors in the F.P.A. seminar, I was aided in this presentation by helpful comments from several colleagues at the Tavistock Clinic. The final responsibility for the manner and matter of the monograph is mine.

I wish to express my thanks to Mrs. D. Gonda and Mrs. L. Martin for their accurate typing of the manuscript; Mrs. Martin also recorded all the seminar sessions in shorthand

and prepared the typescripts that provided the raw material for this book. I am indebted to Mr. A. S. B. Glover for his thoroughness in compiling the index.

I hope this book will foster the growing awareness among doctors of the importance of psychotherapy in medical practice and contribute to the understanding of a clinical problem that has never before been discussed at length.

London, June 1961   LEONARD J. FRIEDMAN

ACKNOWLEDGEMENT

Thanks are due to Thomas Nelson & Sons for permission to reproduce the passage from *Adomnan's Life of Columba* that appears as an appendix.

CHAPTER 1

Origins and Aims of the Study

That a woman may need a doctor's help before she can have sexual intercourse after marriage may be surprising. Newspapers occasionally report the annulment of unconsummated marriages, but these seem rare. The drive to have sexual intercourse has powerful instinctual sources. When it is supported, in marriage, by strong cultural and social values as well, one might think that only the most severe organic pathology could block this drive. For most people this is true, but occasionally emotional conflict completely prevents sexual intercourse.

Couples suffering from this problem are loath to reveal it even to their doctors, thereby denying themselves the possibility of help. Doctors share the general belief that the problem is extremely rare. Their training has not prepared them to handle it effectively when they discover it. Schooled to look primarily for organic pathology, doctors mistakenly tend to treat this complaint as if it were due to local causes, or lamely dismiss the patient after hearty reassurance that all will go well by itself in time, or perhaps suggest a few drinks before bedtime.

To help such a patient, the doctor must be able to practise

1

'whole-person medicine', not 'diseased-part-of-the-body medicine'. He then recognizes illness as part of the patient's way of dealing with aspects of her[1] life in which physical and psychological factors intimately interpenetrate. In a fundamental sense, he must remain a biologist, a student of life in all its complexity. He must understand that the patient who consults him has complicated and often conflicting emotions and fantasies about her body and its workings and about the people in her life. An important part of mental life goes on outside awareness, strongly influencing conscious thoughts and actions. She has been shaped by myriad life experiences since birth; her current style of living is a complex function of all that has gone before. This approach to the patient as a whole person is as old as medicine and yet is still a research area.

The work reported here is the fruit of a collective effort. The Family Planning Association (F.P.A.) is primarily concerned in its clinical work with providing advice and instruction in contraceptive techniques, as well as investigating and treating problems of infertility. Clinics were established for these purposes. Doctors working in F.P.A. clinics found that some patients were attending who were in need of help with a broad range of marital problems. A few F.P.A. doctors met privately in 1951 with Dr. Joan Malleson (whose published work on vaginismus and non-consummation is discussed in Chapter 2) to discuss questions arising from their work. Requests from this group and other sources to F.P.A. Headquarters for some assistance in dealing with their patients' marital problems led to the recognition that some special training for this work was desirable. Late in 1957, the F.P.A. requested Dr. Michael Balint to undertake the training of a selected group of doctors to increase their skill in dealing with

---

[1] For the sake of clarity in pronoun usage, general discussions throughout this book will refer to the doctor as male and the patient as female.

2

certain types of marital problems which patients presented.

Previously attempts had been made to refer such patients elsewhere. It soon became apparent that referring these patients to psychiatric departments or to social agencies was not a satisfactory way of dealing with them. London psychiatric clinics have long waiting lists of more seriously ill patients who need psychiatric treatment. Private referral for psychotherapy was rarely possible. Unlike the situation in some major cities in the United States, where a growing number of psychiatrists practise briefer forms of psychotherapy based on psycho-analytic knowledge but differing from psychoanalysis in technique, depth, length of treatment, and degree of personality change produced, in London there are hardly any psychiatrists practising what in America is called 'psychoanalytically-oriented psychotherapy'.

Full-scale psycho-analysis was out of the question for patients in this series, with rare exceptions. Even if it were financially possible for them, most could get the degree of help they wanted without the use of a technique which aims at extensive and deep changes in personality structure and functioning; they would not have the motivation to undertake psycho-analysis.

Most British social agencies do not consider the treatment of marital problems their main task. The Marriage Guidance Council does, but their work is carried on by volunteers who lack intensive professional training. The psychiatric social workers of the Family Discussion Bureau (London) work exclusively with couples who have marital problems, but the number of patients attending F.P.A. clinics who needed such help was far greater than the Family Discussion Bureau could cope with. To meet its responsibilities to these patients the F.P.A. needed to develop a new approach.

Early in 1958, Dr. Michael Balint began the series of seminars on which this book is based. The aim was to combine research with training to further the understanding of the problems presented by this group of patients and the special methods and skills the doctors needed to help them. A further question was the method to be used in training the doctors working in F.P.A. clinics. By and large they are general practitioners with a special interest in the specific medical problems of women. A few have had gynaecological training. At the time the seminar started only a few had had some training in psychological medicine as members of one of the Tavistock Clinic's seminars for general practitioners.

The ten doctors in this F.P.A. seminar, all women, were carefully selected from a number of senior medical officers already working in various clinics. One is a fully qualified gynaecologist. The others are general practitioners with a major interest in the specific medical problems of women— what in American usage would be called 'medical gynaecology'. This terminology is not used in England; it would appear a contradiction in terms, since gynaecology is a surgical speciality. Their field of interest includes, but is not limited to, those problems which women have with their genital organs and their functioning, such as infertility or vaginitis. It also includes the psychosexual problems of women, such as frigidity and unconsummated marriages, and of course it includes the fitting of contraceptive devices.

This is a seminar in which all of the members are active contributors, and it is time to introduce them.

Dr. Margaret Blair is a general practitioner with a major interest in medical gynaecology, a field in which she had had 6 years' experience when the seminar began.

Dr. Rosamond Bischoff focuses on medical gynaecology and obstetrics in her general practice, and had had 22 years' experience before joining the seminar.

Dr. Sylvia Dawkins had more than 30 years' experience in medical gynaecology at the start of the seminar; she has worked with the F.P.A. for over 20 years. For the past 10 years she has done F.P.A. work exclusively.

Dr. Alison Giles was in general practice for 8 years; following this, for 10 years to date, she has worked exclusively for the F.P.A.

Dr. Ruth Lloyd-Thomas, a general practitioner with a major interest in medical gynaecology, has had 8 years' experience of F.P.A. work.

Dr. Eileen Mallinson, a maternity and child welfare medical officer, had been interested in medical gynaecology for 15 years when she joined the seminar.

Dr. Eleanor Mears had had 17 years' experience in medical gynaecology at the start of the seminar; the first 5 of these years were in the context of general practice, after which time psychosomatic gynaecology became her exclusive interest. She had had some Jungian analysis at the beginning of her medical career.

Dr. Jean Pasmore, a general practitioner whose major interest is medical gynaecology, had had 24 years' experience before attending the F.P.A. seminar; she had been a member of a general practitioners' seminar prior to this.

Dr. Mary Pollock is a fully qualified gynaecologist particularly interested in F.P.A. work who had had 17 years' experience before the seminar was formed.

Dr. Rosalie Taylor had had 25 years' experience in medical gynaecology when the seminar began; for the first 10 of these years it was combined with general practice, but then became an exclusive interest.

Dr. Michael Balint, psychiatrist and psycho-analyst of over 35 years' experience, has been a prolific contributor of clinical and theoretical papers to the psycho-analytic literature. In addition to his work in psycho-analysis *per se*, Balint has been deeply involved in developing new approaches for training general practitioners in psychotherapy based on psycho-analytic knowledge. For nine years before the F.P.A. seminar began, he had been conducting a series of seminars with general practitioners. This work continues; Balint and several analytic colleagues at the Tavistock Clinic currently conduct a number of training seminars for general practitioners. He has published a book discussing this approach entitled *The Doctor, His Patient, and The Illness* (1957a). A further expansion of these ideas occurs in another book written with Enid Balint (1961). Balint has also presented certain aspects of his work with general practitioners and its implications for the training of medical students in psychotherapy and psychosomatic medicine in several articles (1954, 1955, 1957b, 1960).

The F.P.A. seminar was designed to assist these doctors in dealing with the psychosexual problems of their patients, an area in which their previous training had been deficient, as is all medical training along traditional lines.

One method of training non-psychiatric physicians in psychotherapy is to give them a course of lectures with collateral reading covering descriptive psychopathology, aspects of psycho-analytic knowledge and theory about mental functioning and personality development, combined perhaps with discussions of interviewing technique. This is not Balint's approach. He does not believe that such courses are of much value. To quote from his 1954 paper on training general practitioners in psychotherapy:

'The results of these courses have been generally disappointing. This is a surprising outcome, for the general practitioner of some years' standing is a very good trainee. He has had time to assess the value and limitations of what he has learnt at his medical school and hospital, he has also had a fair amount of frustration and success in his practice, and he has seen enough of human suffering to make him sensitive. . . . The reason for the failure of these courses

6

would appear to be that theoretical lectures, even when based on, or illustrated by, case histories or clinical demonstrations, hardly give more to the general practitioner than what he can get from reading books. Strongly influenced by the traditional medical training based on lectures and clinical demonstrations, both practitioners and psychiatrists forget, in a mutually attractive teacher-pupil relation, that psychotherapy means acquiring a new skill and not learning some more theories and facts. Nothing is easier or more satisfying for a psychiatrist than to take a patient's case and deliver a lecture about the theoretical implications, the unconscious dynamisms, and the likely diagnosis of the patient. Moreover, such teaching is gratifying indeed to both. The specialist can shine, and the practitioner feels enriched and reassured. But this gratifying collusion is disappointing in the long run because in reality it is too facile and does not give the means of effecting therapeutic changes.

'Instead of allowing this teaching-being-taught atmosphere to develop, the aim of such a course should be to help the practitioner to acquire a new skill. This means a considerable, though limited, change in the personality of the doctor. The doctor has to discover in himself an ability to listen to things in his patients that are barely said, and, in consequence, he will start listening to the same kind of language in himself. This fairly difficult change of attitude is not needed if the doctor does not have to do the listening himself, but is taught and told what other people have found out about the "human mind"—namely, the theories of psychodynamics, of personality development, of transference patterns, and so on. In the same way as a new physical skill can be learnt only in the actual situation while dealing with the problems in it, so is it with the acquisition of psychological skill. This is why concentrated full-time

7

courses lasting for some weeks have proved to be of limited value. The general practitioner must use his own current experience as a basis for learning the new skill.'

The F.P.A. project, therefore, was organized as a weekly two-hour seminar at which members presented current case material from their practices for discussion. The proceedings were recorded verbatim in shorthand by a stenographer, who then prepared typescripts from her notes. These records were the raw material for this book. At the time of writing, the seminar has met more than a hundred times and is continuing to meet.

The aim has been to enhance the doctor's sensitivity to what is going on consciously and unconsciously in himself and in the patient when they are together; this demands a kind of listening which is quite different from the traditional medical 'history-taking' approach. The doctor must develop an awareness of certain automatic patterns of response in the patient and in himself, patterns that are only partially related to the current reality of their relationship, coloured as they are by emotional events from earlier life.

Quoting again from Balint's paper (1954):

'. . . the doctor . . . must become aware of his own automatic patterns and gradually acquire at least a modicum of freedom from them. Intellectual teaching, however good and erudite, has hardly any effect on this process of liberation and general easing up. What is needed is an emotionally free and friendly atmosphere in which one can face the experience that quite often one's actual behaviour is entirely different from what has been intended and from what one has always believed it to be. The realization of this discrepancy between one's actual behaviour and one's intentions and beliefs is not an easy task. But if there is good cohesion between the doctors in the group, the mistakes, blind spots, and limitations of any individual member can be brought into the open and at least partially accepted by him.'

In his 1960 paper Balint wrote:

'The doctor must be able to observe and, still more important, report about his observations to the seminar. It is easy to state that his observations must be conscientious and his report sincere so as to enable the seminar to get a realistic picture of what has happened between doctor and patient. This, however, is not a simple task because every report is followed by a fair criticism of the doctor's methods and, over and above it, by interpretations of why he said or missed something and made the correct interventions or the mistake he made. When it is realized that our skills as well as our mistakes and blind spots are expressions of our character and personality, it will become clear that a frank discussion of them goes far beyond what is required from a student during under- or even post-graduate medical training. Hardly any one of us is so healthy that he could stand unruffled a searching criticism of his professional behaviour and the showing up of some of his shortcomings and blind spots, yet this is to be accepted in our seminars; moreover, after listening to all the criticism of his handling of the case the doctor is expected to return to his patient and test out in the subsequent therapeutic work whether the seminar was right or he himself. This is perhaps the most difficult task, for most of us like to prove, at any rate to ourselves, that after all it was we who were right and the seminar and its leader were wrong when criticizing us. On the other hand, it is almost equally difficult to avoid humbly and penitently accepting that of

course one was wrong and all the others, especially the
great leader of the seminar, were absolutely right. It is a
hard school to learn not to be swayed too much by either
of these powerful emotions and to conduct the subsequent
sessions of the psychotherapy so that they might throw
some light on the various problems and show at what point
and how much the doctor was right and how much his
colleagues in the seminar or its leader.'

Returning to his 1954 paper:

'It is a fact that acquiring psychotherapeutic skill is
tantamount to discovering some hard and not very pleasant
facts about one's own limitations. This unpleasant strain
must be faced, and the group develops as long as it can face
up to it, and stops developing as soon as it tries to avoid it.
It is the task of the group leader to create an atmosphere
in which each member (including the leader) will be able
to bear the brunt when it is his turn to bear it.

'It is a precondition of our technique to establish this
kind of atmosphere in the group, and it is only in such an
atmosphere that it is possible to achieve what we term "the
courage of one's own stupidity". This means that the doctor
feels free to be himself with his patient—that is, to use all
his past experiences and present skills without much
inhibition . . .

'Perhaps the most important factor is the behaviour of
the leader in the group. It is hardly an exaggeration to say
that if he finds the right attitude he will teach more by example than by everything else taken together. After all, the
technique we advocate is based on exactly the same sort of
listening that we expect the doctors to acquire. By allowing
everybody to be themselves, to have their say in their own
way and in their own time, by watching for proper cues—

that is, speaking only when something is *really* expected from him and making his point in a form which, instead of prescribing *the* right way, opens up possibilities for the doctors to discover by themselves *some* right way of dealing with the patient's problems, the leader can demonstrate in the "here and how" situation what he wants to teach.'

The material presented here is a result of the devoted efforts of all the participating doctors to help their patients with ever-increasing skill and sensitivity. All have been frank and open in their seminar discussions and have had the courage to participate in the lively, personal give and take which goes on. This has involved considerable exposure of aspects of their own personalities. Just as disguise is needed in presenting patients' material in print, the doctors in the seminar must appear later in the book under pseudonyms. In the clinical section of this book, all names of both seminar doctors and patients are false names, invented to preserve their privacy. The usual psychiatric conventions have been followed in case discussions, with the deletion and change of details of personal history that could be identifying but are not essential to the understanding of the case.

In the F.P.A. seminar the doctors have discussed a variety of psychosexual problems presented by their patients. This book is limited to a presentation of their work with cases of non-consummation. Such cases are not rare in their practices. The average estimate the doctors gave of the number of virgin wives each of them saw in a year was 25–30. The lowest estimate was 8–10, the highest, 50–60. Granting that these figures are approximate, the 10 doctors probably saw about 700 cases of non-consummation during the two and one half years of this study. Of these, 100 were reported to the seminar for discussion. These were not a random sample of the total. Cases were not chosen according to any explicit policy. Retrospectively, the doctors all believed that they tended to report those cases they found difficult, since they wanted to increase their skills. The definition of 'the difficult case' varied somewhat from doctor to doctor. It also varied over time; patients who seemed difficult to treat in the early months of the work later would have seemed easier, as skill increased. Occasionally cases were reported because they illustrated some point of current interest. Thus, 18 cases were first reported after treatment had been successfully completed. There is thus no way of accurately assessing how well the patients reported represent the total population of patients whose marriages are unconsummated. All things considered, it seems a fair assumption that the overall ratio of success in treating such cases by the methods used would be somewhat higher than that in the cases reported here.

Before presenting the details of this work, the viewpoints of other workers in this field will be summarized in the next chapter, to place what follows in its proper context. Chapters 3, 4, and 5 present clinical material from selected cases, organized to illustrate some attitudes and personality trends that are common in these patients. These often occur in combination, so the attempt to separate out typical personality types is admittedly somewhat artificial. In the discussion of these cases, some working principles of treatment will be presented. In Chapters 6 and 7 case material is used to illustrate aspects of treatment technique. Chapter 8 presents data compiled from the whole sample of 100 patients, and Chapter 9 summarizes the main points of the preceding sections.

Occasional sections of the seminar discussions are presented to give the flavour of the training method used. It must be emphasized that no one can expect to acquire the skills necessary for this type of work by reading this or any other book. Supervised experience with patients is necessary for the acquisition of such skills.

CHAPTER 2

Review of the Literature

The problem of unconsummated marriage is not mentioned in standard psychiatric textbooks (Arieti, 1959; Ewalt *et al.*, 1957; Henderson & Gillespie, 1956; Mayer-Gross *et al.*, 1960; Noyes & Kolb, 1958). Although the problem is emotional in origin in most cases, such patients are more likely to consult a gynaecologist than a psychiatrist. However, standard textbooks of gynaecology say little about women who experience difficulties in sexual intercourse and even less about the woman who has not consummated her marriage. This chapter presents a survey of relevant material from gynaecology texts and from articles in the medical literature, for contrast and comparison with the work of the F.P.A. seminar.

Several words used in discussing difficulties of sexual intercourse merit brief comment.

Non-consummation generally means that there has been no entry of the penis into the vagina; sometimes it is used when only very shallow penetration has occurred, which may be sufficient to rupture the hymen, but full penetration has not occurred. Pregnancy may occur despite non-consummation; sometimes semen deposited at the vaginal orifice impregnates

13

a woman; some women who become pregnant with intact hymens have inseminated themselves with a syringe.

Dyspareunia, derived from the Greek for bad bedfellow, refers broadly to any sort of pain or difficulty experienced during attempted coitus. Sometimes it includes non-consummation. Some authors use the word *apareunia* for non-consummation, limiting the application of dyspareunia to cases where partial or complete penetration has occurred with accompanying difficulty or pain. A distinction sometimes made between primary and secondary dyspareunia is ambiguous: at times the reference is to the presence or absence of organic lesions; at times the usage distinguishes difficulty from the first attempt from that which begins after a period of successful intercourse.

Vaginismus is a symptom complex which may cause dyspareunia (including non-consummation), but the categories of vaginismus and non-consummation do not overlap completely—some women are characterized by one but not the other.

Kroger and Freed (1951) give a clear description of the findings in cases of vaginismus.

'When these patients are examined, the mere attempt or actual touch of the labia may produce spasm and pain. The introitus may become so constricted that it entirely prohibits the entrance of the tip of the finger (or during coitus the penis). The spasm may involve the perineal muscles alone or may constrict the levator ani right up to the vaginal fornices. Accompanying the spasm there is a marked adduction of thighs, even to cramp-like spasm of the adductor muscles. Reich refers to these muscles as the "pillars of virginity". Invariably the lumbar spine is extended in the position of lordosis. Frequently the posture

14

assumed is one of opisthotonos, with the head bent backward. These symptoms are not only present during coitus, but can be witnessed during the attempted examination.'

Frigidity refers to a woman's failure to experience complete gratification during sexual intercourse, usually implying an absence of vaginal orgasm. It may vary in degree from complete vaginal anaesthesia during coitus to lesser degrees of impairment of pleasure. It does not necessarily imply either dyspareunia or vaginismus.

We are now ready to consider what the textbooks say about the problem of the virgin wife.

The three-volume work by Rubin and Novak (1956) contains no mention of non-consummation. Wharton's book (1947) treats the topics of vaginismus and dyspareunia in a brief section which mentions only physical causes and ignores unconsummated marriages. MacLeod and Read's *Gynaecology* (1955) remarks on dyspareunia due to 'neurotic temperament' but only to suggest psycho-analysis or hypnosis, stating that the prognosis is always guarded.

The textbook by Curtis and Huffman (1950) recognizes the problem only as an anatomical one and advises drastic measures.

'Dyspareunia of the virgin, including "honeymoon dyspareunia", includes the largest group of those who suffer from pain at the introitus during the sexual act. Every girl who contemplates matrimony merits consideration of whether the vaginal orifice is sufficiently roomy to permit intercourse without unjustifiable suffering. A hymenectomy is seldom of material moment in affording relief, for the hymen is usually readily torn. An orifice which is too tight because of a firm perineum is a different matter. A perineostomy may be a relatively simple operation; but frequently it should be extensive and demands exacting technic'.

They then describe the technique.

Novak and Novak (1956), in their section on local causes of dyspareunia, mention the persistence of a rigid hymen; they cite one case of a woman married ten years who had an intact hymen. In their opinion such cases are not rare. In discussing vaginismus, they write: 'In some cases *overdilatation of the canal* under light anesthesia is necessary, particularly in the case of new brides in whom the hymen has remained unbroken. This is not an uncommon condition, and every gynaecologist of experience has seen patients in whom the hymen has remained unbroken after many years of married life.' Again, the problem is treated as a purely anatomical one.

Peel's text (1960) gives the reader an impression that more is involved than this. This book has a section on coital difficulties which discusses vaginismus as a cause of primary dyspareunia and recommends hymenectomy only if the hymen is rigid or if tender, inflamed tags remain. 'In the milder type of case the gynaecologist by careful and sympathetic handling of the patient can overcome the difficulty. She may be persuaded to pass graduated vaginal dilators under supervision until she can take the maximal size. By then her confidence is restored and she can have normal coitus. In some, however, the psychogenic disorder is very deep seated and ingrained and only prolonged treatment from an expert psychiatrist can help the patient.' The patient rather than her hymen alone is clearly being considered here, although she remains a rather abstract entity.

Janney's book (1950) carries this approach somewhat further. The doctor is told to discuss feelings with the woman with dyspareunia. Fear, feelings of guilt, and loss of confidence in her mate are listed as emotional causes of difficulties in sexual intercourse. Advice and reassurance by the doctor are considered helpful. Non-consummation is not indexed but is explicitly discussed (pp. 177–8): 'Within recent months I have seen in my practice three patients who have been married for considerable periods without having accomplished intercourse.' In one case a woman married for two years came with this as her complaint. She had an unruptured hymen and a very considerate husband. She had been ignorant about sexual matters prior to marriage and did not know that intercourse might be uncomfortable at first. After she had been taught the technique of stretching her hymen with her fingers the marriage was readily consummated. Janney was not successful in treating two other cases, one of two years' and the other of nine years' duration. Both wives were antagonistic toward intercourse, rejected the doctor's suggestions for treatment, and failed to return. In one case the husband was also seen. He was inconsiderate and boastful about sex, 'undoubtedly a contributing factor in his wife's fear of complete intercourse'.

In discussing this Janney writes: 'These represent a crystallized attitude, antagonistic to sex and any sexual adjustment, which may make itself apparent in increasing degrees as the maladjustments become of longer and longer standing. In my experience these problems require psychotherapy, which I do not feel qualified to give.'

Jeffcoate's textbook (1957) takes a broader view than the others. In the introduction to his book he states:

'The development of the highly specialized gynaecological surgeon advances operative technique but may also engender a narrow and harmful outlook. Such a specialist can become a craftsman first and doctor second, yet the woman who seeks advice for discomforts related to the genital organs is not usually in need of an operation: her need is understanding—understanding of the whole woman, her outlook, her achievements and failures, her domestic and social problems. . . . A gynaecologist must in any case be a psychologist although not necessarily a trained psychiatrist.'

This book contains a chapter on problems of sex and marriage with sections on the consummation of marriage, the grounds for annulment, and problems of apareunia and dyspareunia. He writes:

'Both partners are concerned in dyspareunia . . . Disparity in size between the male phallus and the vagina is often alleged by the woman: this is only a theoretical possibility because the normal introitus and vagina adapt themselves to any circumstances. Some women who suffer dyspareunia omit, through embarrassment, to mention it unless asked a leading question. Ignorance, too, can result in failure to disclose apareunia and it is quite common to see women who have been married for many years without the partners realizing that they have never had coitus other than coitus inter femora.'

Jeffcoate cites vaginismus as the commonest and most important cause of dyspareunia: 'generally it is a functional disorder which is seen in the highly strung and over anxious woman who may be physically attractive but spoilt'. He lists the important causal factors as 'faulty sex education; ignorance; initial painful and clumsy attempts at coitus; an unfortunate experience such as criminal assault, or even the administration of an enema in earlier years; hysterical hyper-aesthesia of the vulva and thighs; fear of pregnancy; fear of childbirth; and the use of contraceptives.'

He discusses his treatment of an intelligent, attractive, imaginative nurse who remained virginal after four years of marriage. After several interviews she revealed that she had been in an operating theatre during her nursing training when

18

a foetus was delivered by embryotomy; the mutilated body was handed to her to hold. She was appalled and since then feared childbirth although she desired children. Treatment consisted of promising delivery by caesarian section should she conceive and still desire section at term, training in relaxing the pelvic floor (she had severe vaginismus), and the use of graded vaginal dilators, accompanied by discussions of her fears. 'It took many months for her outlook to change but she conceived within one year of her first visit. . . . The cure was not complete, however, because even though she became more normal as pregnancy advanced, she insisted on the promised caesarian section.'

Jeffcoate advises practitioners faced with a patient with vaginismus to study her 'nervous makeup, her outlook on the problem and her reaction to a gentle attempt to make a one-finger vaginal examination.' What happens next seems out of keeping with what he wrote earlier in his book. 'If it is clear that the patient is unlikely to co-operate, it is best to desist at once, to allay her fears and to explain that the entrance to the vagina is so narrow that it requires dilatation under anaesthesia.' Following this procedure, he uses graduated dilators repeatedly, first inserted by the doctor or a nurse and later by the patient. 'The real purpose of these instruments is not to dilate the vagina further but to convince the patient that her trouble is corrected and to give her confidence.' Dilatation under anaesthesia is not used when the patient is less anxious and 'more reasonable'; instruction in sexual anatomy and pelvic muscle relaxation is then combined with the use of dilators. The greater the doctor's skill, the fewer are the patients who require general anaesthesia, he writes.

Turning from the general textbooks of gynaecology to two books dealing with the psychosomatic approach in this speciality, we find that Wengraf (1953) very briefly mentions vaginismus in the section on frigidity and does not discuss non-consummation as such, although it is mentioned in the course of one case history.

Psychosomatic Gynecology, by Kroger and Freed (1951), contains no explicit discussion of unconsummated marriages, but has a relevant chapter entitled 'Dyspareunia due to vaginismus'. They define vaginismus as an involuntary spasm of the vaginal muscles during intercourse which is always psychogenic and represents a defence against the sexual act.

'Although vaginismus is a symptom of hysteria, many of the patients are not neurotic. As a matter of fact, once the spasm disappears, the sexual adjustment of these individuals is often satisfactory, since over one half are able to obtain orgastic gratification. Some other commonly noted psychodynamic factors associated with vaginismus besides dread of the penis, are marked hostility toward men and oedipal conflicts. Nearly all the women we have seen with vaginismus believe that they are "too small inside".'

Kroger and Freed advise referral of difficult cases to a psychiatrist but state that most of the simple cases 'will respond to superficial psychotherapy, if the physician is gentle, patient, and sympathetic in his approach'. They find pelvic diathermy and heated pneumatic dilators helpful occasionally in aiding relaxation. In their experience, many husbands of such women needed instruction in coital technique; many suffered from premature ejaculation and impotence. The results of physical methods of treatment are likely to be temporary, and spasm may return. 'These refractory patients will require individual study and treatment for their anxiety neuroses. The associated frigidity and depression, which are invariably present, are often resistant to superficial psychotherapy as is the husband's secondary impotency which so often complicates the picture. Surgery, though 'cures' have been reported, is contraindicated and without real value, because the underlying emotional conflicts are seldom resolved by it.' They favour hypnoanalysis, and present two cases treated by this method.

It is a curious fact that there is so much variation in the books reviewed. Some authors, by their omission of discussion of difficulties in coitus, imply that the problem is either rare or not the concern of the gynaecologist. Other authors indicate that the problem is not uncommon, but differ about what to do. Some deny its emotional basis, view it as an anatomical problem, and make a surgical attack on the vagina. Others accept its psychogenesis but feel that such patients must be handled by psychiatrists. Some who see it as a psychogenic problem nevertheless emphasize physical methods of treatment. When the existence of 'irrational' factors is recognized, some authors seek to treat the problem by appealing to the woman's rationality by means of educational techniques, advice, and reassurance. Some authors emphasize the husband's sexual aggressiveness which frightens the wife traumatically when coitus is first attempted; others comment on the impairment of the husband's potency. Why has it been so difficult to be clear about this subject? This merits further discussion. First we shall see what more can be learned from articles published in medical journals that discuss non-consummation and the related topics of vaginismus and dyspareunia.

Despite the viewpoint of many current textbooks, the emphasis on psychogenic aspects of this problem is not a new one. In 1909, Walthard, a professor of gynaecology at the women's clinic of the municipal hospital in Frankfurt am Main, published a paper entitled 'The psychogenic aetiology and the psychotherapy of vaginismus'. He gives a good description of the findings on examination, and argues against the view that vaginismus has a purely neural explanation; he

21

believes that it is due to fear and anxiety about pain, guilt about extra-marital coitus, fear of pregnancy, aversion to the husband, and other such 'phobias'. He writes (my translation): 'Vaginismus is not a physiological reflex, but rather a purposeful emotional defence reaction, caused by a phobia— thus, a psychic reflex.' The aetiologic therapy is therefore psychotherapy, 'meaning counselling the patient about the complete intactness of her genitals as well as about the irrationality of her phobia.' He combined this with teaching the patient to relax the muscles in spasm by contracting their antagonists, using the principle of reciprocal inhibition. He reports having used this method successfully for ten years, without the use of dilators or surgery. In his discussion he refers to P. Dubois and Pavlov; there is no indication that he was familiar with the newly emergent views of Freud. Moreover, he states that he has not considered the therapeutic task finished with the relief of the symptom of vaginismus; he has continued to search for other indications of 'psychaesthenic' modes of thinking in the patient's life to help her to alter her 'faulty adjustment abilities'. This further work is prophylaxis against the development of other phobias and the return of vaginismus.

It is clear that no formal knowledge of modern psychology was necessary for Walthard to reach these conclusions. He was presumably a doctor who was willing and able to listen to his patients and learn from them. He recognized the relationship of the symptom to the patient's emotional life and the broader aspects of her personality and treated his patients accordingly. Many later papers fail to reach this level.

Articles in the medical literature dealing with unconsummated marriages are few in number. As in the textbooks, the topic is often absent from discussions of dyspareunia and vaginismus (Berry, 1952; Ellery, 1954; Gliebe, 1942; Griffith, 1943; Hall, 1952; Johnstone, 1944; Kehrer, 1950, 1955;

Marshall, 1945; Reymond, 1951); many of these papers take a limited anatomical point of view. Hall (1952) trains patients with vaginismus to control voluntarily and relax the perineal muscles. Mears (1958) mentions non-consummation and advises that patients be taught to stretch their own hymens, with their fingers or with dilators, aided by the doctor's support and reassurance. Beasley (1947) mentions one case of a virgin wife. He treats vaginismus with the use of hydrostatic pressure in a rubber dilator, warmed a bit higher than body temperature to help relax the spasm. Fagan (1958) emphasizes the doctor's educational task in dealing with couples who have not consummated their marriages. He advises the couple to read a book on sexual technique in marriage. Lloyd (1950) states that many cases of dyspareunia are cases of non-consummation. His approach to the patient combines education with the use of dilators and sometimes dilatation under anaesthesia; difficult cases are referred for psychotherapy. Frank (1948) reports on a 36-year-old woman who had remained a virgin after 13 years of marriage. He excised her hymen. Three days later she made a suicide attempt and her latent psychosis became overt two months later. Mayer (1932), echoed by Smail (1943), warns the doctor about such people in what seems an exaggerated statement for which no evidence is offered. In discussing dyspareunia, Mayer mentions extremely severe forms: 'in the cases of persistent virgins for many years, we must be extremely cautious. They are frequently psychopathic personalities. Interference here is not without considerable danger of a complete breakdown and even suicide.'

Estimates of the incidence of non-consummation vary widely. Kinsey *et al.* (1953) report that there were 'an exceeding few' couples in their series who delayed their first coitus for months or years after marriage or who had never had coitus after marriage. These are largely accounted for by women who never lived with their husbands after marriage, those with physical handicaps which rendered coitus impossible, and those who married homosexual men as a matter of social convenience. This work was based on a sample of 2,480 women who had at any time been married. Phillips (1940) believes that many practitioners underestimate the number, and writes: 'I have come across many scores of these "married spinsters" during years of practice, when investigating some gynaecological complaint.' He treats them by digital dilatation under anaesthesia, or by an operation on the vagina involving the cutting of some circular muscle fibres in cases of vaginismus which have gone on for 'months or even years'. In a series of 2,000 gynaecological patients, von Mikulicz-Radecki (1948) found that two per cent complain of coital difficulties; he believes the true incidence is probably twice as high. In thirteen cases in his series coitus was not possible, because of impenetrable hymen, anatomic malformations, scars, or vaginismus. He relates the latter to trauma at the first attempt at intercourse and advises teaching of sexual technique combined with reassurance.

Malleson (1952) quotes figures based on two series of patients with primary sterility, saying that Stallworthy found an intact hymen in five per cent of 581 hospital and private patients, and Green-Armytage reported this in four per cent of 397 private patients. Frank (1948) does not make an estimate of the incidence of non-consummation but reports that cases of dyspareunia represent one and one-half per cent of his gynaecological practice. Smail's figure (1943) certainly seems too high: 'Roughly speaking, the marriages which are not in fact actually consummated must almost equal the number which result in divorce or annulment.' Perhaps he meant to say that as many unconsummated marriages continue as end in divorce or annulment. He goes on to say, 'Many women are astonished when told that appraisal shows

24

the hymen to be partly or totally intact after years of married life.'

Nobécourt (1942) discusses a royal marriage which was not consummated for several years. Louis XIII of France married Anne of Austria when both were little more than fourteen years old. Contemporary accounts report that on the wedding night they spent two hours in bed together—their two nurses were in the room—and Louis pretended great satisfaction, saying he had consummated twice. Afterwards they slept apart; despite the urgings of his entourage, his confessor, and the cardinal, he refused to accomplish the marital act until three years later. After another three years the queen became pregnant but miscarried. They were separated by circumstances for a time, but nine months after their reunion the future Louis XIV was born. Nobécourt's statement that all this was quite natural because boys younger than seventeen years are incapable of intercourse is astounding. At any rate this case indicates that advice, reassurance, and education are not always effective in cases of non-consummation.

Although flawed by its comments about the dangers of breakdown or suicide in the treatment of married virgins, Mayer's paper (1932) makes some sound points. He states: 'In approaching the treatment of psychogenic dyspareunia, it seems advisable for the time being to forget anatomic considerations and consider the individual.' He emphasizes the importance of treating both marital partners in cases of primary dyspareunia, and records an important observation. 'Incidentally, there is a high incidence of gentle, timid, and inexperienced men, often relatively impotent, among the husbands of these women with primary dyspareunia. Perhaps this is due, in part, to their unconscious selection, on the somewhat mistaken assumption that a gentle person would hurt them less.' He advises the use of graded dilators combined with 'the establishment of confidence and the transference through which the fear, resentment and anxiety are partially overcome'.

Two articles by Malleson (1942, 1954) are important contributions. They are based on her experience with 'hundreds' of cases of vaginismus. (Claye's article (1955) appears to be based on her views.) In her 1942 paper she states:

'It is by no means uncommon for women who have been married many years to seek advice on account of dyspareunia, conjugal dissatisfaction, or sterility, and for examination to reveal a hymen partially or totally intact. . . . It would be difficult to assess whether such cases are due more frequently to failure on the part of the husband or that of the wife; because, although one partner may be initially responsible for the difficulty, more often than not this trouble is, so to speak, "infectious", or at any rate, accentuated by the other partner being under-competent, over-anxious, or too forbearing. This article will deal with those cases in which the trouble comes mainly from the woman's side, on account of coitus being rendered impossible by spasm of the introital vaginal muscles.'

Malleson sees vaginismus to be entirely psychogenic, and explains it to her patients as a flinching prior to a dreaded experience which leads to self-inflicted pain. When, in the course of an attempted vaginal examination, the patient begins to exhibit lordosis and thigh adduction, she stops the examination and tells the patient that nothing further can be done unless she co-operates. 'Every woman with vaginismus tries, unconsciously, to put the blame or responsibility on to the other person: she expects to be exhorted and physically "attacked". There is no quicker way of modifying these impressions than a kindly but firm refusal to show further interest. Hostility should be met by a firm refusal to be drawn

26

in, and a detached civility will often bring quicker co-operation than a warm eagerness to help.'

At this point, the patient usually requests that a further attempt at examination be made. When her lordosis and thigh adduction again begins it is commented on and the patient is told to draw the pelvis up, which relaxes the spasm in a few minutes and allows the painless insertion of two or three fingers. The woman is reminded that her pain is self-inflicted, is given a lubricating jelly, and generally does well. However, many such patients have other problems, so that after they accept penetration their attitude often needs expert psychotherapy.

Malleson reports that 11 out of 20 cases of severe vaginismus gave a history of conditioning to expect pelvic pain as a result of enemas and soap suppositories in childhood. In her experience, at least half of these patients obtain vaginal feeling during intercourse once the spasm is quiescent, and none are entirely anaesthetic. She mentions other trends—dread of the penis, hostility to men—which may make use of the symptom of vaginismus and overdetermine its original protective function, but feels that the original anal trauma is paramount. 'Since the original traumata would have been administered by women, it is possible that the sex of the medical attendant influences the degree of emotion transferred. . . . One might suppose that relaxation is best achieved when the emotional atmosphere differs as far as possible from the original one; so that the attendant, even if unfortunately resembling mother or nurse, should at least refrain from behaving like her!'

In her 1954 paper, Malleson reports a similar approach in dealing with women who have never had intercourse. She adds the recommendation of digital stretching of the hymen by the patient herself or the use of dilators by the patient. In discussing vaginismus in this paper, she advises seeing the husband to enlist his co-operation. 'No woman cures herself of vaginismus by evading coitus and too much sympathy from husband and doctor will not really help her.'

She describes her technique as one of explanation and persuasion which can be used by any practitioner acquainted with gynaecological work who can bear with 'nervous and hostile patients'. 'These measures cure most cases, usually by the second or third interview and very few need to come back more than four or five times. Sometimes a non-consummation of many years' standing can be relieved in one such session. There can be very few neurotic complaints which yield so rapidly to medical measures.'

The work of Michel-Wolfromm is also worthy of detailed review. Her 1953 article reports on seven years of experience in France with both clinic and private patients suffering from a range of psychosexual disorders, including dysmenorrhea, premenstrual tension, dyspareunia, vaginismus, and frigidity. Some of her cases of vaginismus were virgin wives. She writes (my translation), 'Our method of examination and treatment envisages, contrary to classical rules, *simultaneously and synchronously*, both the psychic and the somatic points of view.' Except for a minority of complex cases which were referred to a specialist for psychotherapy, both the psychotherapy and the gynaecological work were carried out by the same doctor. Her justification of this approach is 'the certainty that, without our intervention, these women, appearing stable, would never have had recourse to psychiatry or analysis.'

This paper reports on 24 cases of dyspareunia (22 of them had vaginismus). In one case the husband was almost impotent; in the other cases the husband's ability to perform was normal, although his spirit of enterprise had been adversely affected. 'The husband's shortcoming was ordinarily his *timidity*.' After cure of their vaginismus these patients generally were capable of normal sexual feeling during intercourse.

Michel-Wolfromm presents further details in her 1954 report, which is confined to the topic of vaginismus. She writes (my translation), 'While it is sometimes necessary to resect a resistant hymen or to cure a vaginitis, it is always indispensable to add supportive psychotherapy to the local treatment. This has for its goal the removal of the psychic obstacle which can be translated as a *refusal to accept the sexual act.*' In this series of 22 cases, two patients had impenetrable hymens (after 3 and 12 years of marriage respectively), a fact previously unknown to them. Resection of the hymen was followed by psychotherapy. 'Even if a malformation or an anatomical lesion exists, the admixture of psychic factors sooner or later spoils the effects of treatment' if psychotherapy is omitted. A number of brief case histories are given in this paper.

The patients in this series were generally of above-average intelligence, often with a lively imagination; they had chimeric dispositions or else were very ambitious. Two were of too low an intellectual level to permit psychotherapy. In general they could be grouped into two character types, those with strong masculine tendencies and those with infantile attitudes.

'The masculine character type, very widespread these days, incites the young woman to express her independence and seems to prevent her from passively giving herself to her partner . . . Vaginismus expresses their aggressiveness and serves as a revenge for their day-to-day enslavement. This illustrates what the analysts call their "castration" tendencies . . . They are cured when they have understood why they have been refusing, even if they become neither sweet nor submissive.'

'The infantile attitude, equally widespread, explains the majority of the other cases. . . . They remain attached to their families . . . the father or the mother are the object of an exclusive adoration or a lively hostility.' They all have

29

hysterical characters to varying degrees; the role of the father is dominant in most cases, either because of the attachment he inspires or the jealous hostility towards him. '. . . here again it is the oedipal fixation which most often hobbles adaptation to sexual life.'

Treatment combined the use of dilators with psychotherapy. Graded dilators were used at first, then a diathermy dilator was inserted and left in place while the therapist stayed at the patient's side talking with her. Attempts at intercourse were proscribed during the course of treatment, which rarely lasted more than 12 sessions. This treatment led to 16 cures and was ineffective with the remaining 6 patients. In interpreting the results, the author emphasizes that transference factors are important and that the results are not due to suggestion. 'Sometimes, as a result of psychotherapy, the patient, until then puerile, evolves in a rapid maturation. She learns to liberate herself from a family upon whom she had been too dependant to take her proper role in relation to her husband. Sometimes the revelation of her latent hostility toward her partner liberates her.'

None of the papers reviewed above was written by a psychiatrist. The final one we shall consider is the work of a psycho-analyst, Hilda Abraham (1956). She refers to a 'long series' of cases—the number is not stated—of non-consummation and vaginismus whom she saw on referral from the gynaecology department of the hospital where she worked. The duration of the non-consummation varied from two months to many years; all but one patient were able to permit sexual intercourse after treatment. Her methods are not stated in detail. Patients were seen for a limited number of interviews, which were based on psycho-analytic understanding; apparently this was brief psychotherapy based on psycho-analytic knowledge rather than full-scale psycho-analysis. In treating her patients, Abraham aimed at more than mere consummation: 'In most cases it was possible to help her to a satisfactory, or at least partly satisfactory, marital relationship.' Like Kroger and Freed, Mayer, Malleson, and Michel-Wolfromm, she comments on the frequency of passivity in the husband: 'I have come to regard the frequent statement of such women: "My husband is very good, he doesn't bother me" with a certain dismay.' When the husband has not urged his wife to take some action after several months of unconsummated marriage he might be assumed to have latent homosexual trends.

One case is briefly discussed—a 39-year-old woman who had not yet had sexual intercourse after 10 years of marriage. Her mother had died in giving birth to the patient; father remarried when she was $3\frac{1}{2}$ years old. The patient's stepmother was cruel to her. The patient improved rapidly after a discussion of her fantasy of being 'too small' for intercourse, the oedipal origins of which became explicit. In general her patients were not profoundly disturbed women: '. . . with few exceptions, the women sent to me for non-consummation of marriage and severe vaginismus showed no other serious neurotic symptoms and were able to make object relations.'

Her patients fell into two main groups; in this respect also her observations show some similarity with those of Michel-Wolfromm. The larger group had reached the oedipal level of psychosexual development but were fixated on father. They needed little further help once the first big step was taken; the shift of their attachment from father to husband was not difficult to achieve. They achieved orgastic satisfaction in varying degrees and adjusted quickly to motherhood.

The second group consisted of patients who were fixated to mother. Sometimes they had not reached the oedipal level. When father had been 'weak, quarrelsome, cruel, unfaithful, or unkind from the outset, it may be assumed that, in Freud's

31

words . . . "One has to give full weight to the possibility that many a woman may remain arrested at the original mother-attachment and never properly achieve the changeover to men".' Sometimes this leads to the girl developing a masculine identification, especially characterized in later life by a sadistic attitude toward the husband. She found that patients readily understood this component of their negative attitude to coitus, punishing the husband for father's shortcomings. Abraham quotes Fenichel's view that 'vaginismus may be an expression of the revenge type of the female castration complex'. She mentions similar statements from the writings of Freud and Karl Abraham.

Freud's 1918 paper, 'The Taboo of Virginity' (Freud, 1949), is of some interest in this regard, although it explicitly avoids discussing 'the frequent attempts of women to escape the first sexual act' beyond attributing them 'in the main, if not entirely . . . (to) . . . the general female tendency to ward off sexuality', which scarcely seems a considered statement. In this paper he offers an explanation for the observation that, in some primitive tribes, defloration is carried out by a priest, an old woman, the bride's father, or some person other than the husband, either in infancy, at puberty, or just prior to marriage. This sometimes took place in the course of, or was followed by, a ceremonial act of intercourse with the person who ruptures the hymen, although Freud's anthropological sources were vague about this.

Freud mentions, and largely rejects, explanation of this taboo in terms of a general dread of shedding blood, the dread of novel experience, or the dread of women generally which is expressed by various taboos among some primitive peoples. He mentions some women he had treated who had reported their open expressions of enmity towards the man following coitus, even when they had enjoyed it, and he suggests that some degree of animosity is always present. This is particularly true of the woman's first experience of coitus, for several reasons. The woman feels somewhat sexually devalued after her virginity is lost. The first experience of sexual intercourse rarely fulfils her expectations. Another source of this animosity is related to the degree of fixation the woman may have to the first man she loved in childhood, her father; when this is strong, her husband is in a sense not the right man. Freud also relates this animosity to the woman's wish to have a penis of her own; when this wish is strong in a woman, she may want to castrate the man and keep his penis for herself. He suggests that the taboo of virginity was developed to protect the husband against the archaic reaction of enmity which may be liberated by defloration.

We are now in a position to evaluate the varying approaches of workers in this field. It is common knowledge that the topic of sexual intercourse is guilt-laden and anxiety-provoking in our culture; that difficulties in intercourse are related to problems of anxiety should be self-evident. If we keep in mind the fact that the data presented are revealed in the course of the doctor-patient relationship, we must pay attention to factors in both which influence what happens. Most authors agree that the patient can be expected to have some difficulties in discussing her problem, but we must recognize that the doctor's anxieties may also influence this, and lead to an unconscious collusion with the patient to deny the problem entirely and maintain the *status quo*, or to agree at least to consider the problem as purely physical. We have seen that patients may have the fantasy, 'I am too small,' which has no basis in fact; what effect does it have on such a patient if the doctor shows by his actions that he shares such a fantasy, and tries to make her 'big enough' by means of surgery or dilators? We have heard that some of these patients are full of unconscious anger towards men and wish to damage them in some way. Could this be one of the determinants of the

33

surgical 'attack', or in any case does the patient perceive it as a retaliation for these fantasies? Many of these patients have husbands described as timid, overly forbearing; some were made secondarily impotent to some degree by their wives' behaviour. Is there something in the way these women interact with a male doctor which somehow gives him the feeling that such cases are beyond his abilities and must be referred to expert psychotherapists, that the prognosis is poor, that it is somehow dangerous to try to treat them?

Some of these women profess ignorance about sexual matters; most authors take this literally and play into the defence unwittingly by trying to educate them. Why doesn't the doctor ask himself: How is it possible that she has not found out the facts for herself in the process of growing up? How has she avoided knowing? Why is it important for her not to know?

When fears about being hurt during intercourse or fears about pregnancy or childbirth are elicited, some doctors try to reassure the patient that her fears are irrational. Of course irrational factors are involved, but does reassurance help, any more than it helps the hypochondriacal patient, the patient with frank phobias which she knows to be irrational, or the deluded patient?

Can it be accidental that those authors who have the greatest experience with such patients, who are most sensitive to the emotional implications of their symptoms and to the relationship meanings of treatment, who are prepared to investigate the problem in depth with their patients—that those authors are all women themselves? Or is it possible that, quite apart from any special knowledge of psychodynamics, women have an empathic understanding based on their own life experiences which helps them to work with such patients?

With these questions in mind, we are ready to discuss the work of ten F.P.A. doctors, working in consultation with a psycho-analyst, on the treatment of virgin wives. In the next three chapters, selected cases from the series will be presented in some detail, with summaries of the seminar discussions which followed their presentation to the group. For teaching purposes, I have selected cases that illustrate certain of the personality constellations commonly occurring in these patients. Naturally these do not exist in pure culture, and many patients show varying combinations of the traits to be discussed.

First we shall consider some patients who specialize in the defence of 'not knowing' about sexuality, thereby keeping anxiety-laden sexual feelings out of awareness. I shall discuss the techniques which have been useful in helping patients like this to become more accepting of their adult sexual roles. The following chapter discusses the predominantly aggressive woman, for whom loving and fighting are very much confused. The next chapter considers some women who wished for a baby without intercourse, whose concern for the mother-child relationship outweighed their desire to be wives to their husbands. Questions of therapeutic technique, which are touched on in these chapters, are discussed in Chapters 6 and 7. Chapter 8 presents statistical material describing the entire sample of one hundred patients.

CHAPTER 3

Awakening the Sleeping Beauty

But a whole century asleep, to wait,
And for that long put off the married state—
Where will you now such patient females find?

asks Charles Perrault in the moral he draws from his fairy tale, *The Sleeping Beauty* (Brereton, 1957). We know from the findings of psycho-analysis that many myths, legends, and fairy tales owe some of their appeal to their artful representation of unconscious fantasies related to childhood stages of psychological development. Echoes of some of the psychological problems of virgin wives can be found in this story, which serves as a prelude to the case material.

A royal couple, childless for many years, finally conceived a daughter. A number of fairies attended the christening and magically gave the princess the gifts of perfect beauty, marvellous wit and gaiety, and other desirable feminine qualities. One vindictive old fairy uttered the curse that the princess would prick her hand with a spindle and die. This destiny was mitigated by a good fairy; instead of dying from the prick, the princess would fall into a deep sleep for a hundred years, after which a prince would come to waken her.

Trying to avoid this calamity, the king forbade all his subjects to have or use spindles, on pain of death. One day, when the princess was 15 or 16 years old, she was playing in the castle when her parents were away. In an attic room in a big tower she found an old woman who had not heard the king's proclamation, spinning. 'How pretty it is,' said the princess. 'How do you do it? Give it to me and let me try.' She ran the spindle into her hand and fell into a sudden sleep. When he learned what had happened, the king had the princess placed in the finest room in the palace. The good fairy returned and put everything and everyone in the castle, except the king and queen, into the same sleep. The king and queen left the castle and gave orders that no one was to go near it; rapidly a dense and impenetrable forest grew up which all but hid the castle, the result of another spell of the good fairy, to protect the sleeping princess.

One hundred years later a prince was hunting in the neighbourhood and asked about the towers he could see rising from a thick wood. People told him various frightful tales, but one old peasant had heard the facts from his father and told the prince, who immediately decided to find out for himself. As he approached the forest the tangled growth opened, allowing him to penetrate, but closed behind him so that none of his men could follow. The princess awakened, they fell in love, and married.[1]

[1] If we take the liberty of treating this material as if it were the manifest content of a dream, there are elements suggesting that a defence against incestuous wishes towards the father is involved. The princess cannot consummate until 100 years are up, after her parents are dead, since they are specifically excluded from the long sleep. The original tale also emphasizes that the prince was from a different family from that of the princess. This gratuitous denial of family relationship adds to the suspicion. In the introduction to his translation of Perrault, Brereton points out that there is a tale similar to *The Sleeping Beauty* in the *Pentamerone* of Giambattista Basile. Although published about 60 years before Perrault's story, 'it was written in the difficult Neapolitan dialect and was accessible to very few until it was at last translated into standard Italian in 1747, long after Perrault's death' (Brereton, 1957). This is certainly an independent version of a similar folk fantasy. In Basile's story, at the girl's birth it is predicted that she will be in

In this story, the good and bad fairies can be taken as representations in fantasy of different aspects of mother. The danger from the spindle symbolizes mother's prohibition of sexuality to her daughter. Penetration is a fearful danger. This is carried further in the symbolism of the impenetrable forest which grows up around the castle, finally opening spontaneously to provide a way in for the prince alone. Because of the spell she is under (mother's prohibitions operating unconsciously), Sleeping Beauty's resistances against sexuality are all passive—she is simply asleep and the forest protects her. The end of the spell brings mother's belated permission to enjoy marriage, and no man can enter before then. But while she sleeps, does she perhaps dream of a man powerful enough to penetrate the magic forest, a man violent enough to awaken her from spellbound sleep?

There are levels of meaning behind the story itself. This is also true of what patients say and do. Certain parallels can be drawn between aspects of the Sleeping Beauty story and the problems presented by some patients in this series. Some women who have not consummated their marriages are in a sense asleep; they restrict conscious awareness of sexual feeling. They use the defence of 'not knowing' about their sexual organs to ward off anxiety. Childhood fantasies about their genitals still influence their behaviour, as do childhood prohibitions, fears, and attachments. I shall term the resistance against consummation based on the defence of 'not knowing' the Sleeping Beauty syndrome. Such women tend to think of their vaginas as being too small for the penis and fear injury from intercourse.

great danger from a splinter concealed in flax when she grows up. In her sleep she is seduced by a king and has two children by him. He takes her back to his palace, but he is already married. His wife orders that the girl and their children be served up in a stew, but they are rescued and the king's wife killed instead. (Perrault has a similar ending to his story, not quoted here, involving the prince's mother and Sleeping Beauty). The king who is already married stands for the father. It is clearer in this less disguised version that the latent content is the girl's wish to have father to herself, taking mother's place.

MRS. ABLE

Mrs. Able's case illustrates the Sleeping Beauty syndrome. Her case is presented here in much the same way as Dr. Smith reported it to the seminar. Like many patients in this series, she first went to her family doctor complaining that she could not have a baby after eight years of marriage. He sent her to a teaching hospital clinic for investigation of her infertility, where Dr. Smith saw her.

She was an attractive woman of 33, slim and vivacious, who blushed readily. 'We have been trying for two years to have a baby,' she told Dr. Smith. 'I thought I had some skin covering my passage which had to be broken, and I was surprised when my doctor told me that it was gone.' Her menstrual periods had always been painful, and this condition had twice been treated by dilatation and curettage of the uterus, but she still believed that her hymen was intact. She was ignorant about sex and it had been a great shock to her when her periods first began. She said, 'You know, I still thought babies came out from the navel when I was 18. I didn't know anything. Once when I was 18, I was alone in a railway carriage and a man came in and took his thing out. I was frightened. It was so terribly large.'

Dr. Smith told her that she doubted such extreme naïveté at the age of 18, thereby challenging the patient's defence. Mrs. Able responded by saying, 'Mother never told me anything, of course,' but then added, 'Perhaps I didn't want to know,' indicating the beginning of some insight.

The patient spoke of her husband, two years younger, whom she had known since childhood, as 'a wonderful man.' Repeatedly she emphasized how kind and polite he was. They attempted intercourse about twice a month without success. He had no difficulty getting an erection, but he either ejaculated prematurely or, more usually, not at all. Sometimes she had an orgasm when he stimulated her clitoris. When he tried to penetrate it hurt so much that she cried out, and he gave up trying out of consideration for her. He was going to see another doctor because he was worried about his ejaculation difficulties.

Before she had decided to marry her husband she had thought she was in love with a man much older than herself whom she knew at work. He never took any notice of her. She repeated several times, 'But he wouldn't have been nearly as good a husband as mine,' as if attempting to dispel her own persistent doubts about this.

Her father had always set a higher standard than she could achieve. 'I've always been such a failure,' she said. 'My brothers were clever, but I've always had to struggle. Sometimes I feel that I don't deserve a baby or anything at all. I am so afraid that I am going to be a failure at work that I drive myself. I feel very guilty. Maybe my husband's trouble has something to do with me.'

She agreed to being examined by Dr. Smith and prepared herself for examination in a matter-of-fact manner, but had such severe vaginismus that Dr. Smith could not insert an examining finger.

'Even though you know that you haven't a hymen you are so afraid of being hurt that you tighten up and keep me out, just as you do with your husband,' Dr. Smith said. 'The more you tighten up the more it will hurt.' Dr. Smith told her how to relax her pelvic muscles, and then Mrs. Able could be examined easily. She expressed surprise that the examination had not been painful, and again the doctor commented on her expectation of pain.

Mrs. Able then said that often she couldn't have intercourse because she was so tired after a day's work. She also suffered from chilblains and had to lie absolutely still to prevent them from itching.

41

Dr. Smith said, 'We have had all the excuses. Now tell me the real reason why you don't want intercourse.'

'It hurts. I do make a lot of excuses. Ought I to give up my work?'

The doctor pointed out the patient's wish to be told what to do, which would avoid an examination of the reasons why she was in conflict about these issues. Mrs. Able said that her firm was short-staffed, and she did not dare to give notice. It developed that she was afraid that they would be angry with her for doing so, and this fear inhibited her.

A fortnight later she returned for another session, at which she excitedly told the doctor that they had managed intercourse for the first time several days previously, but on a subsequent occasion her husband was again unable to ejaculate. She also said that she had given notice at work.

To give some impression of the way the seminar works, excerpts from the discussion that followed the case presentation are given in this case and in some of the subsequent ones, based on the transcripts. The discussions have all been condensed. In the interests of clarity I have rephrased some passages with the approval of the participants, preserving as much as possible of the flavour of the discussion. Pseudonyms are used for all the doctors except Balint.

DISCUSSION

BALINT

May I point out a lesson to all of us? There is little point in giving advice to patients. Dr. Smith resisted the temptation to do so. Had she given the patient the advice she sought, Dr. Smith would have deprived her of full responsibility for her own life.

MONROE

I wonder whether she consummated and gave up her work to please you. Perhaps the excitement was in telling you what a good child she has been.

SMITH

I am sure of it. It was as if she were saying, 'I am a good girl; I have done my homework.'

BALINT

As you point out, in some ways she behaved towards Dr. Smith as if Dr. Smith were her mother whom she was trying to please. This was not interpreted, but here it seems to have led to something useful. Perhaps her previous resistance against intercourse was partially based on a fantasy that avoiding it would please mother. In so far as she sees Dr. Smith as a mother, she sees her as a mother who is in favour of her having intercourse. Now let us try to see what sort of people these two are, what sort of relationship exists between them.

SMITH

Her husband is two years younger than she is. He tends to be overly kind and polite, and she encourages this in him.

BALINT

His sexual behaviour shows his inhibition; he tries but doesn't achieve penetration. Perhaps he is too polite, and—to be very brutal—incapable of taking his wife by force.

SMITH

She can't allow people to be angry or aggressive towards her.

A VISITING DOCTOR

Don't you think this is a case where the husband might be seen?

BALINT

We have found that if we can help the woman to change, seeing the husband is not necessary. In quite a number of cases, even after years of non-consummation, the marriage has been consummated after treatment of the wife alone. This may seem quite incomprehensible unless one is willing to believe that women have a very great power over a man's potency. There is no question that if the woman allows her husband to be aggressive, and even enjoys it, it might give more to him than any psychiatric treatment. We agree that to treat impotent men is a very long and difficult task, whereas here in a few weeks we can make them potent by treating their wives—heaven knows how. What should be the main approach in this case?

SMITH

To encourage her to enjoy her husband's aggression.

BALINT

And that she should encourage her husband to be aggressive.

WHITE

You might discuss with her how she always has to be a failure.

BALINT

Yes. There is this undercurrent in her to frustrate and make impotent any man. She provokes aggressive demands and then frustrates them. Men who don't take any notice of her remain on a pedestal. The man who notices her must be knocked down.

BAKER

Her fantasy about the hymen reminds me of some questions I have had from schoolgirls to whom I give sex education talks. They think there is an inner hymen as well as an outer hymen.

BALINT

More and more we find that the fantasy a woman has about her body determines her behaviour in sexual life. May I add one more comment? As long as she keeps this need to be a failure, she can't permit her husband to enjoy intercourse. Very likely this connects with her relationship to father. She resented the high standards of achievement father set for her. If she is a success, father was right. Her unconscious wish is to frustrate him, to show that he was wrong.

At a later seminar, Dr. Smith reported what she had learned from the doctor who saw Mr. Able for a general examination. He was nervous and shy, thought intercourse was only for the purpose of pregnancy and felt it to be wrong otherwise. Now that they were trying for a baby, intercourse was acceptable. In the first years of marriage he was not able to penetrate and therefore, he said, he could not get an emission because there was no stimulation.

Since his wife had been seen the second time by Dr. Smith, he said they had been having intercourse every night; his ejaculation difficulty had disappeared. The examining doctor expressed surprise and Mr. Able said, 'It's all right, isn't it—can't I?' He found his wife quite easy to penetrate now and he was enjoying intercourse thoroughly. The doctor advised him to decrease the frequency of intercourse a bit lest his sperm count drop too low at the fertile period. About three months later, Mrs. Able reported that she was pregnant.

It is clear in Mrs. Able's case that her 'ignorance' about sex would not have responded to ordinary educational approaches. She needed not to know, for emotional reasons. Such sleepers need to be awakened to their bodily feelings, which they have largely kept out of awareness. One useful technique in helping such a woman integrate the feelings arising in her sexual organs with her conscious mental image

45

of her body is to encourage her to explore her vagina with her fingers. This procedure also tends to reverse childhood prohibitions which have continued to act as an unconscious barrier to genital pleasure.

MRS. WILLIS

With Mrs. Willis, this technique helped her to consummate her marriage after 17 years, the longest time interval in the series. She was 37, her husband, 38.

Dr. Evans reported:

The interesting thing there was that she didn't seem to be very worried. They were good friends, very much in love, and had gone on like this having heavy petting and mutual masturbation. At first she had felt a bit agitated, but the feeling passed. The desire for children was dormant, and they didn't seek advice until she heard from a friend about a case like hers which had been successfully treated. She showed no sign of strain. I had a simple talk with her as I would with someone who came right after marriage. I put her on the examining table, and encouraged her to explore her vagina with her finger. She said, 'Oh, that's where it is— fancy that!' Mother had never told her anything. She had a small vagina, hymen intact. She returned in a fortnight to say, 'I have just come to tell you that it is perfectly all right now. We had intercourse that night and everything is fine.' They had been having it practically every night since. I examined her again and found the hymen ruptured; the vagina took two fingers easily. She was quite sure that her husband was penetrating fully now. I saw the husband outside and he shook my hand and off they went, saying that they hoped to have a baby very soon.

DISCUSSION

STANLEY

Like the princess who is awakened by a kiss.

46

BALINT

Prince Charming in the shape of Dr. Evans!

WHITE

You make her seem naïve and childish.

EVANS

Adolescent, rather. Both of them seem a couple of nice kids. What struck me about her was that she just didn't know where her vagina was.

BALINT

But why don't they know, and what does it mean to them? When you want to eat you don't need to ask where your mouth is.

STANLEY

Almost as if they feel not grown up enough, still in the nursery.

BALINT

A rather frightened woman picks up a frightened husband, half impotent, and the two have an agreement that they don't bother much about each other—that I can understand. But after 17 years, that they then start off and have intercourse several times a week is extraordinary! We must try to understand this better in subsequent cases, to find out what leads to such a dramatic change.

MRS. RANDELL

Mrs. Randell's case is a final illustration of the defence of 'not knowing' about her body. She too expected intercourse to be a painful, violent act. Before seeing Dr. Stanley she had seen a psychiatrist several times because of her fears of intercourse. She was a 22-year-old primary school teacher; her husband was seven years older, and they had been married for two years. About once a week they had attempted coitus. As he began to penetrate she complained of dreadful pain; out of consideration for her he stopped, lost his erection, and never finished with an emission.

Dr. Stanley reported:

He would like to have intercourse when she is having a period, but they never do; or in the morning, but it isn't possible because she has to rush to do her housework before going to her job. I asked whether she really needed to work; she said she didn't, but she was afraid of letting the school down. I said she wasn't irreplaceable. She thought she might give it up next year—'But of course if I were pregnant I would leave tomorrow.' She felt she couldn't allow herself the leisure to enjoy intercourse, although she would like to be at home. He brings her to orgasm by caressing her breasts, never by touching her clitoris or vagina; this is the same way she used to masturbate when she was single. I said. 'You feel that your body is only all right above the waist. You behave as if your genitals don't exist.' Mother was always kind to her but didn't tell her much. Mother had severe asthma and was advised against having further pregnancies after the patient's birth. Her parents were happy together. Father died of a heart attack 7 years ago.

When her periods started she thought menstruation was so awful and dirty that she had to get mother to wash her down. She thought of a period as the egg coming away and bringing all the dirt with it. She always seemed to have a curious lack of interest about herself and never found out any more. I asked if she made love with the light on. No, she liked her husband to know that she felt passionate but wouldn't like him to see her.

I tried to examine her and at first she had a spasm. Then

48

she relaxed and I was able to put two fingers in. I got her to examine herself and she inserted one finger, then two, three, and four. She was very surprised. Then she told me she always felt the pain was due to a hymen a little way inside which had to be broken; her husband got as far as this 'hymen' and couldn't get any further. She was very surprised to learn that she didn't have a hymen. I think her husband must have penetrated a little way when her vagina went into spasm. Later on she said, 'I think I know what was wrong. I always thought that the opening of the bladder was the opening of the vagina, and that it was so small he was unable to get in.'

DISCUSSION

BALINT

I think she felt there had to be violence and blood before she could be made into a woman, and she can't accept the fact that it had happened.

STANLEY

Then she said the real trouble was mother-in-law. She opposed the marriage, and warned them against having children until they were nicely settled. The patient used to have the most violent rows with mother-in-law and now she stays home when her husband visits her. I said that when he wasn't very potent she felt his mother had made a poor job of him.

BALINT

This shifts the responsibility to mother-in-law; the question is, what is the patient herself doing to reduce her husband's potency?

STANLEY

Closing her vagina. I also spoke a lot with her about her wish to be dumb and not to find things out. To me the most

49

striking feature of her case was her determined ignorance about her body.

BALINT

It is interesting that you leave out her expectation of violence, her disappointment that there was none, and perhaps her fear of violence. She defends herself against this by making her husband impotent.

Dr. Stanley later reported that the marriage had been consummated.

These three cases illustrate the general approach the seminar doctors have developed for awakening these sleepers, who use the defence of not knowing about sex to find a compromise solution for sexual conflict. Initially their approach to the fearful patient had been one of facile reassurance, quite useless since it prevented the patient from discussing her fantasies in detail and coming to terms with her conflicting wishes and fears. Based on this experience, they now try to interpret the patient's conflicts rather than to reassure her.

Educating the patient who professed ignorance of the facts of sexual anatomy and physiology was sometimes attempted in the early days of this work. The doctors soon found that the new knowledge failed to have the desired impact. Sometimes the patient even forgot what she had been taught from one session to the next. Such 'forgetting' was a dramatic demonstration of the repressive forces at work in these patients. Here again, experience led to the abandonment of a primarily educative approach in favour of an interpretive one.

A crucial aspect of their approach is that it is both psychological and physical. Typically the gynaecologist examines his patient but tends to ignore the psychological implications, whereas the psychiatrist avoids examining his patient physically. Combining the psychological and the somatic approach to the patient, as the seminar doctors do, allows the doctor to examine the patient and talk to her at the same time. The examination experience is highly charged with emotion, and if it can be discussed as it is occurring, the doctor has a splendid opportunity to help the patient to come to terms with her feelings and fantasies. Were the doctor a man, the situation would be quite different. Practical considerations require the presence of a nurse when a man does a pelvic examination, which makes psychotherapy more difficult. A great deal would depend on the nurse; it would be easiest to use a technique like this if the nurse had some experience of psychotherapy.

Inviting a woman to discuss her sexual feelings while the doctor is examining her vagina is quite a different matter when the doctor is a woman. The homosexual feelings aroused in the woman-woman situation are apparently more tolerable to both parties (perhaps because they are more readily kept out of full awareness) than the heterosexual feelings stimulated when a man examines a woman. Since there are no men from the F.P.A. in this seminar, we have no direct experience of this in cases of non-consummation. Recently some of the doctors in the seminar have reported interviews they have conducted with men complaining of potency problems, and the resistances against extending the combined physical and psychological approach to this work became apparent.

The three cases discussed here sound the first notes of another theme which will be developed further, that of the neurotic collusion between husband and wife which stabilizes a pathological behaviour pattern in a marriage. A high proportion of the husbands of virgin wives are described as kind, considerate, polite, and understanding. When these sexually inhibited women use these terms, they imply that their husbands are sufficiently inhibited in masculine assertiveness to tolerate and sympathize with their wives' refusal of intercourse over long periods of time. Often they are rendered impotent to some degree by their fears of hurting their wives when they complain of pain as penetration is attempted, perhaps also fearing that they may be hurt in retaliation. Sometimes they are impotent from the start. The wife's attitude to intercourse has a powerful effect on the husband's ability to perform; repeatedly in this series the husband's potency has improved after his wife alone has been treated. Presumably a more accepting attitude on her part reduces his anxiety to a tolerable degree. What the outcome would be in a parallel series of cases in which the husbands alone were treated by men using similar techniques is an interesting question. Perhaps some day this experiment will be performed.

CHAPTER 4

Gentling Brunhild

Das Nibelungenlied, the famous German epic, provides us with another prototype, in Brunhild. The quotations are from Margaret Armour's prose translation (1952). Brunhild was a queen of great beauty and strength. Any man who wished to woo her had to beat her in three tests of strength. '. . . her love was for that knight only that could pass her at the spear. She hurled the stone and leapt after it to the mark. Any that desired the noble damsel's love must first win boldly in these three games. If he failed but in one, he lost his head.' Many men had perished in the attempt.

Gunther wished to marry her, but doubted his ability to win these contests. Siegfried, who loved Gunther's sister Kriemhild, agreed to help Gunther in return for his promise to give Kriemhild to Siegfried in marriage. Earlier in the story, Siegfried had taken a magic cloak, the Tarnkappe, from Albric the dwarf. When he wore it he was invisible, protected from all blows and spear thrusts, and his strength was that of twelve men.

When Brunhild, who knew Siegfried's heroic reputation, saw the retinue arrive, she first assumed that he planned to woo her himself; she revealed her ambivalent wish towards

53

him by saying to her attendant, 'If stark Siegfried be come into my land to woo me, he shall pay for it with his life. I fear him not so greatly that I should yield me to be his wife.' Siegfried pretended that he was Gunther's vassal and she agreed to a contest with Gunther. 'If he have the mastery, then I am his wife, but let him fail in one of them, and ye be all dead men.'

The trial of strength began. Siegfried had slipped away to don the Tarnkappe, and returned invisible, at Gunther's side. Brunhild was '. . . armed, as she had meant to do battle with all the kings of all the world.' When he saw her, one of Gunther's brothers exclaimed, 'We be dead men, for thou wooest the Devil's wife!' But invisible Siegfried withstood the spear she threw at Gunther and hurled it back, shaft first so as not to kill her, 'and her strength failed before the blow'. In the remaining contests, she flung a great stone and leapt after it; unseen, Siegfried did better in both, bearing Gunther with him. And so the bride was won.

A double wedding was held, at which Brunhild again betrayed her feelings for Siegfried; 'The king and Brunhild were seated, and Brunhild saw Kriemhild sitting by Siegfried, the which irked her sore; she fell to weeping, and the hot tears ran down her bright cheeks.' She explained that these were tears of shame that Gunther's sister should be marrying a vassal.

On the wedding night, 'With Siegfried all went well. He caressed the maiden lovingly, and she was as his life.' But Gunther's struggles with Brunhild began anew. 'He would have caressed her sweetly if she had let him. But she was so wroth that he was dismayed. He thought to find joy, but found deep hate.' Gunther tried to overpower her but she won the struggle, only releasing him after he promised not to touch her.

The next morning he told Siegfried of his humiliation. Again

Siegfried agreed to help him. He used his cloak of invisibility to come to their room that night, taking Gunther's place. When invisible Siegfried approached Brunhild, she immediately began to fight with him. After a mighty struggle he subdued her. 'She said, "Noble king, let me live. I will make good to thee what I have done, and strive no more; truly I have found thee to be my master".' Siegfried then left, and Gunther, with whom Brunhild had thought she was fighting, returned. Thus was Gunther's marriage to Brunhild consummated with Siegfried's help.

The legend is very clear in its description of the aggressive, masculine woman whose competitive feelings towards men drive her to fight them, whose sexuality is thoroughly mixed up with destructiveness. At another level, she desires to be overpowered by a heroic man, a man who must be superpotent to succeed, since she makes ordinary men impotent. Only then can she become submissive; to submit to a man, to want to give herself to him out of love, is not possible for such a woman, because, to her, submission implies admitting inferiority. Relationships between the sexes become a power struggle for her. What love she is capable of is admixed with simultaneous hatred towards the same person.

When the group of men first approached her palace, Brunhild assumed that Siegfried was coming to woo her, and her reactions at the wedding indicate that, in marrying Gunther, she felt she was taking second best. Siegfried's ability to become invisible is a crucial element. In dreams, the invisible man, the man whose face cannot be clearly seen, the man who is not recognized, is often a symbol for the father (or secondarily, the therapist). These elements suggest that another source of Brunhild's aggressiveness towards men is a persistent unconscious attachment to father, an attachment which was so frustrating that she reacts vindictively to all men (compare Freud, 1949).

Although there is no material in the legend to support this, a frequent finding in aggressive women of this type is an underlying intense attachment of a special sort to mother. Mother tends to be the dominant person in the family, and the mother-daughter bond is intensely ambivalent. The daughter remains fearfully dependent on the mother. She cannot risk the added strain on this relationship which would result from loving men, and therefore competing with mother and risking being rejected by her. Her aggressiveness towards men is a way of protecting her tie to mother.

None of the women in this series was as openly aggressive to her husband as Brunhild, but many were covertly involved in similar struggles. A superficial sweetness was a cloak almost as effective as the Tarnkappe in hiding their underlying destructiveness. Mrs. Holmes was one of these patients, and effectively misused the psychological knowledge she had gained from her extensive reading to defeat the doctor initially as she had defeated her husband. This was no small feat, since Dr. Smith was so skilful at reflecting their aggressiveness back to women like this that the seminar borrowed her name to describe the technique, calling it 'doing a Smith' (see Chapter 6).

MRS. HOLMES

Mrs. Holmes, 35, came with her 33-year-old husband, a solicitor. They had been to other doctors about their non-consummation, but never together. Later the wife was seen alone. They had been married for ten years. Just prior to marriage, Mrs. Holmes went to her general practitioner who reassured her that everything was all right. For the first four years of their marriage they did not want a child, so they convinced themselves that their failure to achieve intercourse did not matter. When they decided to have a baby, she had seen a doctor at an F.P.A. clinic a few times, who again reassured her but to no avail. She told Dr. Smith that her parents were happily married. She was an only child. Mother was intensely Victorian in her attitude and had told her nothing about sex, except to suggest, when her periods first began, that this was something a woman had to put up with. Having read books on the subject and discussed it with her fiancé, she married feeling confident that she would have no difficulty sexually. Dr. Smith asked her if intercourse hurt. In front of her husband, Mrs. Holmes said, 'Oh, yes, the entrance hurt. At first my husband tried and got a good erection, but slowly I have defeated him. He is a wonderful husband, so patient and kind. I don't think he ought to be. He's quite a tough person really.' She said this in a condescending manner. Her husband reacted to this by protesting that he only gave in to her on minor matters. Mrs. Holmes challenged this; while appearing to blame herself by saying that she had to watch out lest she be too bossy, her manner seemed almost triumphant. Mr. Holmes said that he did not feel that she was too bossy.

Her mother had dominated the home she said, but they were happy. In a rather patronizing tone, she remarked that father was 'such a demonstrative, amusing, kind man. Mother was rather "sex is nasty". I remember well the words, "Take your hands away from there!" '

Mr. Holmes's parents had separated when he was 14. His mother frequently wept and said that he must never be cruel to women as his father was. Mr. Holmes said that he felt their problems with intercourse had something to do with this; it always hurt his wife and he felt he must never be cruel.

They both insisted that fear of pregnancy made them do nothing in the first four years of their marriage; they accepted mutual masturbation as a substitute for intercourse. She said the trouble was that they both tried to solve all their problems intellectually. When asked if she still feared pregnancy, she said, 'Of course, don't all women?'

Prior to marriage she had had many boy-friends. During her courtship she had engaged in heavy petting with her future husband, afraid to go further. She had been afraid of marriage, but her husband had insisted despite her fear.

After her husband had left the consulting-room, examination revealed an intact hymen and severe vaginismus. Dr. Smith helped her to relax and encouraged her to examine herself. The patient said, 'I still remember mother saying, "Don't touch!", but I have put my finger in previously. I don't mind doing it, but I don't seem to be very effective at stretching myself.'

Ending the case report, Dr. Smith commented on her own feelings at the end of the interview, both a feeling of being let down and a feeling of optimism. She felt that the patient had somehow prevented her from making genuine emotional contact with her.

Opening the case discussion, Balint suggested that when the doctor felt something in the interview, she should have stopped and reflected on it, trying to understand it as a symptom of the patient's illness. (This idea will be expanded in Chapter 6.) In this case, the patient made the doctor feel just what she made her husband feel: completely defeated and still optimistic. As the discussion proceeded, emphasis was placed on the quietly aggressive way in which Mrs. Holmes made her husband both figuratively and literally impotent. Her behaviour suggested that she had strong unconscious castrating wishes towards men. Dr. Smith was criticized for not recognizing these tendencies in her and was encouraged to confront the patient with the malevolence concealed by her

apparent sensible co-operativeness. Her façade of reasonable-
ness had deceived the doctor, just as it had her husband.
Although both of them felt her underlying destructiveness,
neither had openly acknowledged it or taken it seriously when
the patient came close to admitting it. Instead of accepting
this quality in her, the doctor had reassured her that she was
a nice woman.

One doctor wondered whether it would have been sound to
interpret the patient's aggressiveness in the presence of her
husband. Balint suggested that this was desirable and might
have encouraged her husband to be more assertive, although
little change in him could be expected without intensive
therapy, since he had tolerated her behaviour without protest
for ten years. If the patient and the doctor both openly
accepted the patient's hidden malevolence rather than trying
to explain it away, possibly the patient would have more
control over this tendency in the future and would be able to
behave less destructively.

Several months later Dr. Smith gave a follow-up report.
When the patient came back alone for her second visit, she
had dilated her hymen so that it easily admitted two fingers,
but had not had intercourse. Dr. Smith made use of what she
had learned in the discussion, and said to her, 'You seem to be
a very strong woman and you have managed to reduce your
husband to impotence. If you are so strong, perhaps you can
restore him.' Then Mrs. Holmes went on holiday. She wrote
to Dr. Smith to tell her that they were both happy that they
had achieved complete intercourse at last. The discussion
ended like this:

SMITH
Knowing all the answers, how is it that she couldn't apply
what she knew?

BALINT

It is one thing to know and something else to have somebody who can talk about it with you and understand it. It happens so rarely in life that you have a person who understands what you are up to and openly faces it with you. That is what we can do for our patients, and it is an enormous thing.

As with Brunhild, the need for control is important in some of these patients, and they use refusal of intercourse as a weapon in the struggle for power with their husbands. Often this power struggle re-enacts what happened in the parents' marriage. Mrs. Wilson's case, reported by Dr. Smith, illustrates this.

MRS. WILSON

She is 21, married about 18 months. Her husband had written to the Marriage Guidance Council complaining that his wife refused to permit intercourse. She would not agree to see the counsellor on the ground that he was a man, so they sent her to me as a consultant; she came very reluctantly. Her mother was the dominant person in her family and Mrs. Wilson resented her. Father timidly went along with what mother said, and the patient despised him for this. She felt that she was an unwanted child, since she was born soon after her parents' marriage and mother complained that she was thus forced to give up working. Mother had always told her to keep away from men. I asked if she wanted a baby. She supposed so, eventually, but she was afraid of childbirth and a baby would be inconvenient now. Was it fear of pregnancy that made her refuse intercourse? 'Partly,' she said. I told her there was more to it than that.

She said that on the first night her husband tried to put

60

on a sheath and she felt the whole thing was ludicrous. From then on every attempt he made met with disaster. She said she didn't like the sheath, and then, unexpectedly: 'When I was eight years old I found a matchbox with a sheath in it. I washed it and blew it up like a balloon and my aunt gave me a beating for it.' I asked how she felt about males. When she was five she and a little boy undressed and showed each other what they were like; she was beaten and put to bed. She then spoke of how she despised her father; 'mother runs rings around him.' Her thoughts turned again to her husband, how she fights him and pushes him away when he approaches her. When I began to examine her I said, 'Now you are going to fight me.' She had used tampons and had no hymen but a strong vaginismus. I said, 'You are using these muscles to fight with. Do you want to?' No, she didn't. I said she could be fitted with a cap if she wished. I told her how to stretch herself with her fingers and how she could try to control the spasm.

She came in two days later, beaming; they had had intercourse the previous night. I said, 'Why?' She said, 'I remembered what you said—why didn't I go to him instead of waiting for him to come to me.' (I don't remember saying that.) She hung her head and went bright scarlet and said, 'I sort of seduced him.' She was very pleased with herself, but I did not feel this was the end.

DISCUSSION

BALINT

Let us discuss what you did.

STANLEY

It seems to me that you allowed her to be the man of the two, and as long as she is the man she is all right.

SMITH

And she is going to have a cap too, which gives her control of the situation.

STANLEY

Did she enjoy intercourse?

SMITH

No, but it didn't hurt.

BALINT

That is what you have to work with, that she can do everything as long as she is in control.

SMITH

She accepted penetration, so she did accept the male, but on her own terms. I saw her husband outside, a nice, rather gentle creature.

BALINT

You have to allow her to realize that she must be in control and leave it to her whether she wants to go on being like her mother or whether she can ease up a bit and have a different sort of relationship in her marriage. I think she will take her lead from you, although reluctantly. You now know how to work with the apparently frightened woman who is in fact domineering and controlling. You expose her, she understands that you understand, and you get on excellently.

The atmosphere established in these interviews is clearly different from that of medical history-taking. The doctors ask a minimal number of questions, aiming instead at encouraging the patient to talk freely, commenting on what she says. The kind of data which are important in this work are not likely to be gathered by series of questions. The answers to questions can provide certain factual information, but this is at the expense of the wealth of emotional connections which can be made when the patient begins talking freely. The doctor who asks questions merely gets answers.

It may seem paradoxical that some patients, like Brunhild, fear being overpowered by a man and fight vigorously against it, while at the same time they desire this to happen, feeling contempt for the man they defeat. Such conflicting tendencies do exist within the same person; her love and hate are simultaneously aroused and she has difficulty distinguishing between them. In such marriages, a running battle over the years sometimes passes for true devotion. When the husband is in similar conflict, quite a stable equilibrium can be maintained by the unconscious collusion of both partners.

People with depressive character structures are particularly likely to create such sado-masochistic relationships. At depth they feel themselves to be unlovable; they struggle to convince themselves that this is not true. In their relationships with people they tend to be insatiable in their demands, since nothing is ever good enough to assuage this underlying feeling of worthlessness for very long. They then grow to despise people who love them and often succeed in turning this love to hate. By their behaviour towards the loving person they often elicit the rejecting responses they fear but feel they deserve, thereby continuing the vicious circle. When this pattern is combined with specific envy and rivalry towards men, when any assertiveness by the man stimulates the woman's need to cut him down rather than her receptivity, we find a woman resembling Brunhild. The case of Mrs. Davis illustrates some of these elements.

MRS. DAVIS

Mrs. Davis saw Dr. Smith just once immediately prior to the patient's return to Australia. She was 35 and had been married for 14 years, without having had intercourse. Previously she had been treated at the gynaecology department of a teaching hospital and had psychiatric treatment there. Initially she seemed a colourless person, lacking animation, apparently uninterested in the whole problem, but this behaviour changed in the course of the interview. Several years ago she had briefly become acutely depressed.

Father was a strict disciplinarian who ordered the family about as though they were in the Army. She married her husband because father had ordered her to, after insisting that she break her engagement to another man. Fearing father's wrath, she married her husband, but said she had never loved him. After marriage they went to live with her aunt. When he attempted intercourse she began screaming and he could not go on because her aunt would hear her. After she had been married a year she consulted a doctor about her failure to consummate; he performed a hymenectomy. Later, another doctor operated to change the position of her retroverted uterus. She remembered vividly that a foreign nurse who gave her a douche at the time said, 'How funny you are made!' She felt there was something queer about her inside, so that she had to have these operations.

She told Dr. Smith that she did not really want intercourse and never had. When Dr. Smith asked about her feelings toward the other man she had been engaged to, the patient said that she had wanted intercourse with him and had found it terribly difficult to refuse him. They did not have intercourse because she was afraid; her parents had always told her it was wicked.

DISCUSSION

SMITH

By this time we had reached the stage when she was beginning to offer things instead of just answering questions. Her face changed and she became quite animated.

STANLEY
Was she bitterly regretting that she hadn't had an *affaire*?

SMITH
Regretting she had given in to father and not married the first man.

BALINT
She is punishing herself and her husband for what she missed by having been so careful with the first man.

SMITH
I asked her whether the first man would have put up with this if she had married him and she said, 'Not for a moment!'

BALINT
This man deserves her. You could have brought out her malice.

SMITH
I asked if her husband wants to consummate the marriage now. She said he is more concerned about her illness. 'I nag and scream at him and am awful to him, but I think he really loves me because he puts up with me.' She said she was sorry for him. I said, 'Because of what you have done to him?' By now she was showing quite a lot of feeling. She didn't care either way about having a baby. There were three elder children in her own family. When she was 14 years old a brother was born. She said she hated him but worshipped the ground he walked on! It puzzled her that she hated her brother and her mother so much. When she was young there were fearful rows at home. Father was jealous and accused mother of being too interested in the children and in other men.

The patient said she was quite ignorant about sex when she got married. I said she knew something. Then she said that

65

when she was a small girl the father of one of her friends used to play with her genitals when she went to tea there. This upset her very much. Quite out of the blue she began speaking about a recurrent nightmare. 'I am in a house that I remember well from my childhood. There is an attic which is very light but I have to get through a very dark tunnel. I always get stuck. The funny thing about the tunnel is that it's square.' Quite without thinking I said, 'It's very funny made.' She agreed and laughed, and became much more light-hearted. I didn't go into that any further.

BALINT

You are given something highly interesting and exciting but you avoid taking it up!

SMITH

She had never told the psychiatrist she had seen about her dreams when he had asked her; she can't tell men. She said, 'I can talk to women but not to men. It's father; he bothers me so, I'm so frightened of him.' I said, 'The only man you can bear is your husband, who is so kind and gentle, like a mother.' She agreed. I said, 'The other man wouldn't have put up with this; you were afraid of him, that's why you couldn't have intercourse with him.' She said, 'No, I want someone who won't put up with this nonsense. I wish my husband weren't so afraid of hurting me.' Then I said, 'Do you always have to live with relatives so that you can scream?' She said, 'That's funny, we went to Australia and I thought it would be better there in a house of our own, but I couldn't bear it and we had to go and live in apartments.' I said, 'So that you could scream and fetch someone to protect you!'

BALINT

Dr. Smith went on excellently and got at this 'funny made' fantasy. No man can know about it. This woman needs someone who looks after her and isn't a man; she is afraid of a man. How can we respond to this very interesting material?

STANLEY

Perhaps this woman can't forgive the man for not guessing that she wants to be raped.

BAKER

She is very afraid of her inside.

BALINT

She is afraid of the man who makes demands, and hates him. She despises the man who doesn't make demands, and hates him. She is afraid of her inside. She hates everything. She is a typical depressive character who feels there is nothing good in the whole world. The baby-brother she hates is the baby father gave to another woman. Father wasn't so aggressive as the other little girl's father was. She hated and rejected everybody, and all the doctors were made as impotent as her husband.

SMITH

Now she is escaping back to Australia. She said, 'I have never been able to talk like this before. It's such a help. I wish I could come again but I have to leave on Tuesday.'

BALINT

I would have asked if she could postpone the flight. This woman must be treated very firmly.

SMITH

I asked her if she would like me to examine her so that she could know something about this passage which she thought was not made right. She did have vaginismus, but as soon as I told her to pull tight and let go she relaxed quite easily. She asked me to show her how to stretch. I said she could do it

F   67

with her fingers, but what about her fears about her inside? She asked if it was all right, and I said it wouldn't help her if I said it was. I told her the operations were attempts to get somebody else to do things for her. Did she want to have intercourse? She said, 'No. I am sorry for my husband; I've offered him divorce, separation—I don't know why he wants me to go on.' I said she had a low opinion of herself and believed that he couldn't love her. She said the funny thing is that he does.

BALINT

I would have said, 'You must have a low opinion of him because he loves you in spite of everything. Anybody who loves you will be treated in a similar way. Nobody is allowed to love you.'

MONROE

She had a new experience with Dr. Smith.

BALINT

That is the pity, that the uniqueness of this experience wasn't brought out. Even the possibility of creating something was defeated by her postponing her visit to you until the last moment.

Gathering together some of the ideas which these cases illustrate, we find that Mrs. Holmes's case showed again the futility of reassurance given to a patient who is in difficulty. She had been told that everything was all right just prior to marriage and again after four years of marriage, but nothing happened. The deeper implications of her doubts were not explored at the time. Only after her destructiveness towards her husband had been faced could something new happen, ten years after marriage. When the doctor tries to reassure he only succeeds in reassuring himself, not the patient.

When the patient complains that something is wrong with

her, something *is* wrong, although her attribution of the locus of difficulty may be mistaken. The doctor must be able to decode the patient's communications, understanding that she may express her feelings that she is not a proper woman in terms of feared pathology in her genitals. The first two doctors who saw Mrs. Davis and performed various operations on her failed to appreciate the fantasy meanings of her complaints. Her fantasies about her body are part of the patient's inner reality and are powerful determinants of her behaviour.

Another point which Mrs. Holmes's case illustrates is the importance of the doctor being aware of what he feels himself while he is working with the patient. Sometimes doctors develop a protective insulation from the patient's emotions which leads to a rigid and insensitive approach. The doctor's task is the difficult one of remaining in his professional role while preserving his sensitivity to the patient's feelings, since this sensitivity is essential to the doctor's empathic understanding of what the patient is telling him. Though it is crucial that the doctor attend to what he is feeling, it is also crucial that he should not act on these feelings but rather understand them as vital clues to the patient's style of dealing with the important people in her life. In this sense, what the doctor feels is a symptom of the patient's illness, and needs to be understood.

Repeatedly in our cases we see how the patient unwittingly re-enacts, in her relationship with her husband, aspects of her childhood relationships with mother and father, reactions against them or identifications with them. The same thing happens in her relationship with the doctor. When these repetitive behaviour patterns have been consciously acknowledged, the patient is freer to behave differently. The focus must be on the 'here and now', on current behaviour in the marriage and in the treatment setting, which can then be understood in terms of the past.

CHAPTER 5

The Queen Bee

A few virgin wives in this series were also virgin mothers. Either by themselves or with the help of a doctor, they had impregnated the ovum without having intercourse, by injecting their husbands' semen into their vaginas with a syringe. Clearly their relationships with their husbands were strange indeed, in some ways like that of the queen bee with the male. Most of the bees in a hive live a sexless life. There is one female, the queen, who produces all the eggs. The few male bees exist only to fertilize the eggs. After copulation, the male bee dies; he is simply an expendable carrier of sperm for the queen bee.

Other patients had not yet acted on the wish to become pregnant without coitus, but came to the doctor to request artificial insemination with their husbands' semen (AIH). One patient reported an unsuccessful attempt. She had been given dilators by a previous doctor and had been trying to impregnate herself by dipping the dilator in her husband's semen before she inserted it.

A woman who requests AIH may be in despair because her wish for intercourse as well as her desire for children has been frustrated by her husband's complete impotence, which may have been refractory to treatment. At times artificial insemination may be the only realistic solution to an otherwise hopeless problem. In other cases, the wish for AIH may be based less on reality than on primitive parthenogenetic fantasies. It may be a symptom of a severe disturbance in the patient's relationship with her husband. The fantasy meaning of the wish for AIH should be explored with the patient.

It has long been known from the psycho-analysis of adults, and confirmed by direct work with children, that little girls may react to their discovery of the difference between the sexes with envy of the boy. They may imagine that they have been deprived of something which is rightfully theirs. One pathological way of reacting to this is to deny that there is any difference between men and women; an extreme form of this leads to marked devaluation of men. In using their own syringe to inseminate themselves, some women may be acting on unconscious fantasies of this sort.

Very young children frequently imagine that the abdominal enlargement of pregnancy is a kind of getting fat, and think that pregnancy comes about by eating. In such primitive fantasies, intercourse is not necessary to produce a pregnancy; the woman can do it herself. Another childhood fantasy, which may serve to ward off conflict-laden ideas about parental intercourse, is that the doctor does something to make the woman pregnant. Such fantasies may remain active although unconscious in the adult, and may be determinants of the wish for AIH.

The primary attachment to mother may be overly strong and pathological in quality. In requesting a woman doctor to help her get a baby, the patient may unconsciously be trying to get a baby from mother. The mother-child relationship may remain of such importance in the patient's life that her attachment to her husband is shallow and distorted. Becoming a mother can then be an aim which is kept separate from being a wife; the patient wishes to become a mother without becoming her husband's sexual partner. When a woman is driven by primitive fantasies like these, her capacity to be a good mother to the child she desires may be seriously compromised. When the woman's primary motivation in coming for help is the wish for a baby rather than the desire to overcome the inhibitions which have prevented her from accepting sexual intercourse with her husband, the prognosis for consummation is relatively poor (see Chapter 8). This constellation was present in thirty cases in the series. The very few who went as far as to seek AIH represent extreme forms of this; they are discussed in detail because an examination of the extreme case highlights a kind of difficulty which, in lesser degree, was common in these virgin wives.

The case material presented in this chapter all comes from the early months of the seminar, when the doctors were less experienced at eliciting fantasy material and examining the patient's relationships, but these four are the only such cases in the series. The case material illustrates some of the preceding points.

One patient, who was reported very briefly, had come to the doctor requesting AIH after 18 months of non-consummation. Her husband's ability to have an erection had decreased over the months of their marriage and he was quite impotent at the time the patient sought treatment. When asked why she wanted a baby she said she had everything else—house, refrigerator, washing machine—and there was nothing else to go on working for! To her the baby seemed to be another possession to show the world. Her husband was referred to another doctor for examination, which revealed complete aspermia. When this was established, they both lost interest in further treatment aimed at consummation.

73

MRS. CLARKE

More information is available about another patient, Mrs. Clarke, treated by Dr. Jones. The patient began by saying that she wanted to have another child but her marriage had never been consummated. The doctor expressed surprise, and the patient said, 'I impregnated myself. I had gone to an F.P.A. clinic. The doctor there accepted the fact that my marriage hadn't been consummated and said it would be better once I had a child. They gave me a syringe to do it myself. I tried this for several months but it didn't work. Finally I went to a woman doctor who put a little metal instrument inside that pushed the semen in and I became pregnant at once. I've come to see if you will do the same thing.'

She didn't seem at all concerned that her marriage wasn't consummated. She said, 'I know I am all right and I have the child,' and showed the doctor a photograph of her 18-month-old daughter. She hadn't breast-fed the baby; the idea of it had seemed repulsive to her.

She did not mention her husband, and finally the doctor asked about him. He was eleven years older than she, and had no difficulty in maintaining an erection. The patient said they hadn't managed intercourse because she tightened up. She said that it was all her fault. She thought that it must be psychological, and related her difficulty to an experience at the age of seven, when she had been evacuated during the war; a step-uncle had made some sort of advances to her. When the doctor tried to inquire further about this, the patient would only say that he had got too close to her.

Having a child had made no difference in the couple's difficulty in having intercourse. On examination, Dr. Jones found no vaginismus and could easily insert two fingers.

74

The patient had been recording her morning temperatures to determine the time of ovulation, and made an appointment to return with a sample of her husband's semen when she thought she was fertile.

Dr. Jones asked her whether she did not wish to improve her marital difficulties before going further with this plan. Mrs. Clarke insisted that she wanted to have the child first. Dr. Jones told the seminar that she felt extremely reluctant to perform AIH on this patient. She had ended the interview by telling the patient that she might do it for her but that she thought the patient should try to work out her marital difficulties at the same time.

In the discussion it was pointed out that she seemed to want children to compensate for some underlying sense of inadequacy as a woman. Her husband seemed scarcely to exist as a person for her. Dr. Jones added that something in the patient's manner had seemed extremely childlike. Her childhood sexual experience needed further exploration; perhaps, in fantasy, marrying an older man meant marrying this step-uncle. She seemed to create an atmosphere in which she was isolated from deep contact with people. If the doctor acceded to the patient's request for AIH, it seemed likely that she would stop coming as soon as she became pregnant. If Dr. Jones was too adamantly opposed to doing this, the patient might stop coming and find another doctor. The first therapeutic objective had to be one of making a strong enough contact with the patient to carry her through the first weeks of disappointment in not getting what she was asking for, so that she could get something else instead.

Dr. Jones gave another report some time later. The patient had not ovulated when she had thought she would, so she cancelled the appointment but made another one

75

in order to have a talk. The session seemed unproductive. Mrs. Clarke apparently found talking more difficult than she had the first time. Again Dr. Jones tried to persuade her to get treatment for herself as well as trying to get a baby, but the patient said that it was difficult to keep coming because she had to take care of her daughter. The doctor accepted this, fearing that interpreting her resistance might drive the patient away.

Later Mrs. Clarke phoned to say that her temperature had gone down and she wanted to see the doctor that day. When she arrived, she said that she had already inseminated herself but didn't think that it was enough. She had brought her syringe and wanted Dr. Jones to push the semen in higher. Dr. Jones told her she doubted whether it would do any good, but she did what the patient wanted. Then Mrs. Clarke asked to come again the following week to begin treatment.

When she returned she said, 'The first thing I have to tell you is that we have had intercourse twice since I saw you last, but only with me on top, not any other way.' She had not found it pleasurable, nor had she felt any revulsion. She said that she felt that her attitude had somehow changed in the previous few weeks and she had decided that she could not go on living a lie; she wanted to be a proper woman.

Then she told Dr. Jones that her husband had had psychiatric treatment, which had not helped him. Dr. Jones asked her whether she had attempted intercourse in other positions; they had tried, unsuccessfully. Dr. Jones said, 'You can only do it when you are on top, in the commanding position.' The patient agreed. When asked whether she took the lead in everything in her marriage, she denied it; then she said, 'Perhaps I do make the decisions.'

76

In the discussion, the patient's domineering quality was mentioned; after she had triumphed over the doctor by getting her to perform AIH despite the doctor's reluctance, then she could manage coitus. The AIH was also a second triumph over her husband. One doctor suggested that in the patient's fantasy the insemination by the doctor may have seemed a kind of intercourse in which the patient was the woman and the doctor the man, and that when she had intercourse with her husband the roles were reversed. Having consummated her marriage, the patient did not return for further sessions.

MRS. MASON

Another patient stopped treatment without having consummated as soon as she had managed to impregnate herself. Mrs. Mason and her husband were both 29; they had been married for four years. Both did volunteer work with a youth group, advising people who were about to get married. Mr. Mason had had psychiatric treatment for partial impotence for a year without improvement. They visited a fertility specialist who thought that if they had a baby it would help them consummate the marriage, and recommended self-insemination. Mrs. Mason was unable to use the syringe she had been given because of vaginismus, and was referred to Dr. Richards.

They had ceased attempts at intercourse after the first year and practised mutual masturbation. They sought advice only because of their wish for a baby. Mrs. Mason had seen a doctor pre-maritally because she was concerned about possible sexual difficulties, and the doctor had reassured her. When Dr. Richards examined her, the patient had a marked spasm of her muscles. She was very resistant to the idea of inserting her own finger in her vagina, and expressed marked aversion to insert-

77

ing anything inside, but did not mention particular fantasies.

She was an only child and had been very closely attached to mother until she was 16. Since her marriage she had become irritated with mother, feeling that she was narrow-minded and had few interests. Mother had always been extremely concerned about her daughter's health, which annoyed the patient and her husband. The patient knew that mother had had a difficult time during her delivery, with long labour and tense muscles; she had told the patient she had never had another child because of this. She said that she adored her father, but scarcely spoke of him or of her husband.

Prior to marriage she had been afraid that intercourse would hurt. The pain she had experienced had increased her fear.

Her husband, who accompanied her on her first visit, was also seen briefly. He said that he had never been able to talk to his father. Father was away frequently, and mother took charge of his upbringing. She always made him feel guilty when he went out with girls; she was openly jealous of his girl-friends and wouldn't allow him to invite them home. He was so irritated by her that he went into the Army to get away from home. He told Dr. Richards that he still got erections from petting, but when he attempted intercourse he felt as if he were up against a 'brick wall'. He felt that intercourse attempts were more painful to him than to his wife; the pain caused him to lose his erection.

On her first visit, Dr. Richards advised Mrs. Mason not to worry about the syringe, but to concentrate on her more fundamental problems. However, when she returned for a second visit she said that she had used it twice and was pregnant. She was delighted with the pregnancy and said that they hadn't even attempted coitus. As she was leaving she said, 'I am so pleased to think that now I shall be able to help others in the future.' Dr. Richards advised her to continue coming for help with her problems; she said she would, but cancelled her appointment.

The doctors commented on the evident degree of disturbance in both the patient and her husband and on the patient's need to keep her feelings under tight control. Dr. Richards was encouraged to write to Mrs. Mason urging her to return for treatment before the baby was born. The patient replied that they had made a few unsuccessful attempts at coitus but didn't continue for fear of disturbing the pregnancy, although they both realized that it was permissible to have intercourse until quite a late stage of pregnancy. She said she would return if their difficulty persisted after the baby was born, but nothing further was heard from her.

It seems that the husband had left a dominating mother who opposed his sexuality to find a wife who behaved in much the same way. Mrs. Mason seemed to be primarily involved with her own mother, but the details of this were not explored. Perhaps the doctor's concern about her aroused the resentment she felt when her mother was concerned about her health.

MRS. REYNOLDS

The last patient in the series who illustrated some of these problems was Mrs. Reynolds. She had been seen initially before the seminar had begun, and was reported when she wrote Dr. Heath a follow-up letter. She had been initially referred for treatment because of infertility and non-consummation. She was 34, her husband a year younger; they had been married for nine years. After six years of marriage she had had a dilatation of her vagina and had awakened from the anaesthetic during the procedure, which made her vaginismus considerably worse. They had had exterior coitus without penetration through their marriage; her husband nearly always ejaculated prematurely when he tried to penetrate.

Dr. Heath described her as a cheerful, pleasant person who was very eager to have a baby. She had marked vaginismus. Dr. Heath inserted dilators, then encouraged the patient to examine herself and taught her how to relax. Mrs. Reynolds said that she felt that one of the reasons they couldn't have intercourse was that she was very small and her husband was very tall. The doctor advised Mr. Reynolds to see another doctor because of his difficulty in penetrating. The doctor who saw him told Dr. Heath that Mr. Reynolds's difficulty seemed to be psychological; artificial insemination was advised.

When Mrs. Reynolds was seen again, her vagina was well dilated. She thought her husband was somewhat more potent but he still had not penetrated; in fact, he preferred their usual activity. The patient readily accepted the idea of inseminating herself, and became pregnant the next month. This pregnancy miscarried, and she wrote to Dr. Heath to tell her how despondent she was.

About ten months later, she wrote again, saying that she was thrilled to have a baby daughter. The letter, written from hospital, expressed her happiness in glowing terms, but hinted at other things. She remarked that she found it difficult to believe that the baby was really hers after all the time she had been waiting, and she mentioned that she was unable to breast-feed the infant. She closed by thanking Dr. Heath for the help and confidence she had given her.

In the discussion which followed this case presentation, the doctors commented on the lack of information about the patient's relationship with her husband. They thought it unlikely that the marriage had been consummated. Her letter seemed to have been written in a state of euphoria, which masked her underlying problems. Her letter seemed to be thanking the doctor as the author of the baby. One doctor felt that the patient had perhaps been helped to by-pass her real problems, and there might be a risk of her having a more severe breakdown later on. Dr. Heath felt that it was nevertheless better for the patient to have a baby than to go without one. Balint thought that there was too little information to allow a decision as to whether the patient's husband was really so incapable that her choice was the best possible adjustment in the circumstances, or whether psychotherapy could have led to a healthier resolution of their difficulties.

The discussion of these cases appeared to lead to a better appreciation by the doctors of some of the complicated issues which may lie behind the request for artificial insemination. Some subsequent patients were reported who expressed the wish to have a baby without intercourse, but in those cases the fantasies were examined and the wish was not acted upon. One such case is discussed in Chapter 6.

CHAPTER 6

Understanding the Doctor's Emotions[1]

To understand the doctor-patient relationship which develops during this type of treatment, we must take account of what goes on in both doctor and patient and their effects on each other. Previous chapters have focused on the patient, using case material to illustrate typical problems the doctor faces. In this chapter attention shifts to the doctor.

In his professional role, the psychotherapist tries to remain detached from his patient's emotional difficulties so that he may understand them and communicate his understanding to the patient. By his interpretations he helps the patient increase her self-awareness, thereby enlarging the extent to which her living is guided by conscious choice rather than dominated by unconscious forces. The professional detachment necessary for the doctor to accomplish this is quite different from aloofness. It includes sympathy in both senses of the word: feeling compassion for the patient, and also being simultaneously affected by the same feeling as the patient.

The psychotherapist must be able to bear the strain im-

[1] The reader interested in psychotherapeutic techniques is referred to Michael and Enid Balint's book *Psychotherapeutic Techniques in Medicine*, Chapter 6 of which is similar in approach to this chapter.

posed by the patient's unwitting attempts to force him from this position to one of automatic response based on what he himself feels. This is an extremely difficult role to maintain, because the patient presents material which is highly charged with emotion. It is for this reason that a thorough personal psycho-analysis is generally recommended for those who wish to practise psychotherapy. In the course of this the doctor becomes aware of his own conflicts and blind spots. What he has discovered in his own analysis helps him to avoid reacting automatically to feelings stirred up in him by his patients.

Psychotherapy involves an interaction between two personalities. It is important that the doctor be thoroughly aware of his own mental life in order to minimize the extent to which he unwittingly complicates his patient's problems by contaminating them with his own. The same principles of mental functioning apply to the doctor as to his patient. The patient in psychotherapy tends to structure her relationship with the doctor in terms of previous relationships which have been emotionally important to her, especially her relationships with her parents. The complicated mixture of feelings which belong to the patient's relationships with her parents tend to be re-experienced in relation to the doctor. Technically this phenomenon is termed transference. Similarly, there is a tendency for the doctor to react in parallel fashion; this is termed counter-transference. The doctor's counter-transference distorts his perception of the patient and may cause him to act in a manner which is not in the patient's best interests. The doctor who has himself been psycho-analysed is less apt to develop a counter-transference to the patient and more able to understand it when it does occur, thereby avoiding complicating the patient's problems.

Psychotherapeutic skill can be developed only by experience with patients. Until a certain level of skill has been attained, the fledgling therapist needs to discuss his work regularly with an experienced psychotherapist. Reading this or any other book will not lead to the acquisition of therapeutic skill without such experience. It is difficult to learn from unsupervised clinical experience; the beginning psychotherapist will tend to repeat his mistakes without being aware of them.

The procedures described in this book were developed during the course of a continuing supervisory seminar, during which the other seminar members were alert to point out the ways in which the doctor's emotions were influencing the treatment. Repeatedly in the seminar's work, the doctor's natural tendency to become emotionally involved with the patient came up for examination. As a working principle, the doctor was cautioned to examine any feelings experienced during work with the patient, to attempt to understand them as a symptom in the doctor of the patient's illness. This notion that an illness in one person may manifest itself through symptoms in another person is a useful consequence of recognizing the interactive quality of the psychotherapeutic session.

The doctor who begins to experience some emotion during an interview may try to put it out of mind, hoping that if it is ignored this perturbation will disappear so that he can get on with his work. This approach only tends to make it more likely that the feeling will be expressed in a way that is apparent to the patient but not to the doctor. If, on the other hand, the doctor tries to discharge his tension by acting on his feeling, he thereby loses those special opportunities to help the patient which are afforded by his professional detachment. In the interview, the doctor must deal with his own feelings just as he does with those of the patient. He must be fully aware of them, accept them, and attempt to understand them as a symptom of the patient's illness, but not act upon them.

It is most difficult for the doctor to avoid acting on his

feelings when these feelings are sanctioned by the culture patterns pertaining to the doctor-patient relationship.

At first glance it might seem praiseworthy if the doctor is especially kindly disposed towards a particular patient and allows these positive feelings to cause him to be particularly warm and helpful. Some of the difficulties which can arise when the doctor's professional concern gives way to more intense positive feelings for the patient are illustrated in the next case.

MRS. BURTON

Mrs. Burton, a 26-year-old shop assistant, consulted Dr. Stanley after she had been married for two months. Her 30-year-old husband was able to start intercourse but before he could penetrate beyond the vaginal orifice he had to stop because of his wife's complaints of severe pain. She was an only child, born when mother was 34; father was much older. She described her parents as happily married. When she was 14 her menstrual periods began. Mother hadn't told her what to expect but she had had a sex education lecture at school. She thought of a menstrual period as occurring because 'a lot of bad blood accumulates in the womb and has to be got rid of'.

In addition to her request for help because of non-consummation, Mrs. Burton sought birth-control advice. The prospect of a pelvic examination made her very anxious. After helping the patient to relax, Dr. Stanley was able to insert two fingers in her vagina without difficulty; there was no hymen. Mrs. Burton was astonished that the examination hadn't been painful. She was then able to examine herself, but had some difficulty in finding her vagina.

The doctor then discussed the patient's fears with her, and reported as follows: First she said she was afraid of the pain during intercourse. I wondered whether she was afraid that she would bleed. She agreed that she had been very much afraid that her husband would break something and cause bleeding. I then fitted her with a cap, continuing to talk with her during the procedure. She suddenly told me that six years ago she had been rushed to the hospital for operation because of acute appendicitis. When she had opened her eyes after the anaesthetic she saw a black doctor. Seeing him terrified her; she had an unreasonable horror of black people. She was also afraid that they had taken out a lot more at the operation than they said they did. Then she recalled why she was so afraid of black people. When she was a little girl, mother used to threaten to have a black man come and take her away when she was naughty.

After we discussed this she felt relieved and said that talking to me was like lifting a curtain. I then had a long talk with her, making drawings as I explained the monthly cycle. I told her that each month the uterus hopefully prepares itself for a baby, explaining the period in this way rather than in her terms of 'bad blood'. When she left she felt very relieved and I felt she would be all right. I lent her a cap, and she is coming back next week.

The discussion first centred on the patient, then shifted to the doctor's technique. One doctor thought that the educational lecture had suited this young woman, but felt that drawing the pictures had been too much. Dr. Stanley said that she had felt that the patient had wanted to be told all this. She was reminded that the doctor's feelings need to be examined, not acted upon. It then developed that the doctor had felt rather fond of the patient, and she began to wonder whether she had tried to give her a great deal of what she felt was good information, treating her almost as if she had been her own daughter, trying to be a better mother to the patient than her own mother had been. Balint summarized what had happened as a degree of mutual seduction. It had led to a warm, intimate atmosphere which doctor and patient had enjoyed. By giving the patient so much the doctor had deprived her of the opportunity of realizing the answers for herself. He raised the question whether it would have been better for the doctor to maintain a more impersonal attitude while helping the patient to recognize her fear of discovering things independently. Her strong dependent wishes towards motherly women had been partially satisfied by the doctor but not examined.

Several weeks later Dr. Stanley again reported about Mrs. Burton.

She postponed the next appointment twice, for reasons which did not seem compelling, then came in greatly concerned about the difficulty she had had with the cap. She had gone home full of confidence, inserted the cap, then couldn't get it out. She had been frightened, then calmed down, remembered what I had told her, and was able to remove the cap. The difficulty was repetitive; she always had trouble in getting the cap out.

She hadn't mentioned intercourse, so I asked her about it. In a diffident manner she told me she hadn't any difficulty about having intercourse since she had seen me. She said she enjoyed it and had an orgasm, but she didn't seem to want to talk about it, other than to say that her husband thought it was wonderful and couldn't believe that she was the same person. Then she returned to the difficulty with her cap. She also told me an awful thing had happened; a close friend, a woman in her fifties, had died. She felt that this was somehow connected with her having more success, but the connection wasn't clear.

She needed a larger cap. She put it in but could only get it half out. She tried a few times and couldn't do it, so I took the cap out for her and gave her one on which I had sewn a little tag which would enable her to pull it out. She went away terribly relieved about the tag. Intercourse had been successful and I felt I should let her go along on her own now.

The discussion centred on the patient's difficulty with her cap. It appeared that this symbolized her relationship with the doctor. She showed her need to retain her dependent relationship with the doctor by her lack of mastery of the simple procedure of removing the cap. Her dependency had been fostered by the doctor's overprotectiveness. By providing a cap with a tag on it rather than recommending that the patient put one on it herself if she continued to have difficulty, the doctor continued the trend of the first session.

Dr. Stanley then spoke of the special appeal this patient made to her by her helplessness. Dr. Balint suggested that this quality in the patient should have been interpreted to her when the doctor felt like being over-helpful. The doctor's decision to encourage the patient's independence by not seeing her again seemed sound.

One of the doctors asked whether there was any further information about the patient's relationship with the woman who died. Dr. Stanley added that the woman was a person who was always helping people. This piece of information suggests an explanation for the patient's statement that her friend's death seemed somehow related to her own success in consummating. It seems likely that the patient had rather mixed feelings towards older women who reacted to her overtures in an excessively kind and helpful way. She became dependent on them and superficially reciprocated their

89

fondness for her, but also resented them. She could not express this resentment directly for fear of spoiling the pleasant atmosphere which had been somewhat artificially created. It came out indirectly in her cancelling of two appointments for reasons which did not bear scrutiny, her difficulty in learning to remove the cap, and her reaction to the death of her helpful friend, a woman who was close in age to both the doctor and her own mother. She linked her increased success to this woman's death, indicating the strength of her unconscious wishes that the over-helpful doctor-mother should let her be more on her own. Had the doctor preserved her professional detachment, the patient might have been helped to express what may have been one of the central conflicts of her life: that she arranged situations in which an older woman treated her in an overprotective fashion, that her resultant dependence on the older woman was mutually satisfying to a degree, and that she also hated the woman for behaving in this way. It was difficult for her to break this repetitive pattern of behaviour without the doctor helping her to become aware of all its elements.

This case has illustrated some of the difficulties which arise when the doctor acts on his feelings rather than examining them as a symptom of the patient's illness. At times the tendency to react in this way may be strong in the doctor. Although the implications of Dr. Stanley's excessive helpfulness had been pointed out to her in the discussion following her first presentation, traces of it persisted in her second interview with the patient. This underscores the need for supervision while a doctor is developing psychotherapeutic skill.

Positive feelings for the patient may lead the doctor to be excessively helpful if they are expressed rather than examined. What happens when the doctor feels angry with the patient? Owing to an unusual combination of factors, the doctor who treated the following case felt anger and expressed it. The doctor's report on Mrs. Lowe's case gives a vivid picture of what went on between doctor and patient, and therefore is quoted at length.[1]

MRS. LOWE

When I saw this patient I was already in a bad temper following a series of minor disasters which had occurred before I arrived at the hospital. I was late and in a hurry. She brought an unusually long and maudlin doctor's letter. It said how tragic it was that this couple, who would be ideal parents, had not been able to have a child or adopt one. They had fostered a child of five for a few months but the mother had taken it away. Mrs. Lowe was 28, her husband 31, and they had been married for nine years. Her husband was most considerate and pleasant, said the doctor. After 18 months of marriage she had been referred to the gynaecological department of a teaching hospital, where she had refused to allow the doctor to examine her; she failed to keep the subsequent appointment she had been given for examination under anaesthesia. Later she had been examined at another teaching hospital, but had been so terrified by this experience that she failed to keep the appointment they had given her for a post-coital test. Her complaint was of severe pain during intercourse. The doctor added that he had put her in touch with an adoption society, but they had considered her home accommodation unsuitable for a child. In addition, according to Mrs. Lowe, neighbours and relatives were accusing her of being a freak or of having found an infallible method of contraception. According to the doctor she was a poor, persecuted girl, badly treated by everyone. The doctor ended his letter by

[1] The case of 'Mrs. C' (Balint & Balint, 1961, pp. 62f) is based on the same original data.

saying that if she could not be helped to have a baby, he would contact the adoption society to see whether he could help.

Immediately I could hear Dr. Balint saying, 'Be on your guard if a woman is described as an angel!' My first remark to her was, 'Is your house really unsuitable for a child?' She said it was overcrowded; there were only a few rooms and they had two lodgers, although they didn't really need the extra money. I said, 'If this is so, is it going to be suitable for your own baby?' They were going to move, she said. Her manner seemed so insincere that I didn't believe what she told me. When she said that she and her husband had intercourse only once in two months because it hurt her, I pointed out that she had said she had been wanting a baby for nine years and yet refused intercourse. Then I added in a rather cross voice, 'You don't really want a baby, do you!' She burst into tears, sobbing, 'It's horrible, degrading, having intercourse and not having a baby.' She loathed it, fought against it, and wished the baby could be ready made.

I went on to ask her if she had ever really had intercourse. This time she admitted that she didn't think she had. I said in a sarcastic voice, 'Then you don't want a baby. I suppose you know that intercourse is necessary.' At this she said she was so angry with me that she couldn't speak to me. I retorted, 'Angry with me and who else?—the adoption society, everybody.' I told her to get undressed for examination in a cubicle just outside my room, adding that she had a wonderful opportunity to walk out of this hospital too—this time fully justified because I had been nasty to her.

To my surprise she stayed to be examined, but had a marked adductor spasm. I told her in a matter-of-fact way that she would have to separate her legs, and she did. I found a stretched but intact hymen and severe vaginismus. I asked her whether she reacted in the same way when her husband approached her. She said, 'Yes—it's all so horrible! I suppose it's because of my parents. They did this awful thing. We children could hear it though they used to shut the door.' She hadn't known what was going on and had asked her brother. She said, 'I couldn't tell you what he said—it was so awful!' I told her she wanted a baby handed to her on a plate. She said, 'Yes, if only I could have a baby without having intercourse.'

By that time I became a bit friendlier and explained a post-coital test to her. I said that if she wanted a baby she would have to have intercourse, and scheduled the test for her next visit. She had told me she felt appalled about anything to do with her body, such as putting her fingers in her vagina. We made the appointment and she left in tears. I thought she wouldn't return; I had never lost my temper so much with a patient. She was a thin, rather shy, quiet sort of girl.

She failed to keep her appointment, but the following week I found her in the waiting room, crying and agitated because in Sister's absence she had been told by a nurse that she would have to see my colleague. She had protested that she must see me. She had not kept her appointment because her period, which had started right after her first visit, had lasted 12 days, so she decided to come for her post-coital test after three weeks instead of two. She said she had been longing to come and tell me that they had had intercourse twice. The first time was just after her period ended and she was sick afterwards. The night before her visit it had been all right and her husband was terribly happy. This was the first time she had mentioned him. Her post-coital test was good, although the sperm count was somewhat low. There was no difficulty in examining

93

her. She told me more about her childhood hatred of her parents. It seemed that they were always quarrelling. Every Saturday they used to have a violent quarrel and then go into the bedroom, shutting the door. The youngest child, about two, would want to go in. Father would emerge and give the patient money to keep the child out. She couldn't understand why they couldn't go in, although she was twelve at the time. She went away saying that she felt different now and that her husband felt much happier.

In the discussion that followed this presentation, Dr. Smith added that she felt the patient had consummated to please the doctor and also to prove wrong the accusation that she didn't want a baby. Other doctors felt that Dr. Smith's anger had been valuable as an honest expression of feeling, which enabled the patient to express her own pent-up anger. Perhaps she had never been able to have a quarrel with her mother which had led to reconciliation as this one had. Her problems with her husband seemed more related to her difficulties with mother than with father. Balint thought that the favourable results in this case indicated a rare degree of correspondence between the doctor's expression of emotion and the patient's needs. Dr. Smith said she had felt very much on the husband's side, and was angry at the referring doctor for implying that the hospitals had been cruel to the patient. Balint commented on the importance of the psychotherapist having two attitudes at the same time, both viewing the patient objectively and being able to identify with the patient to see the environment from her point of view. Too much identification with the patient had led to the kind of relationship she seemed to have with her G.P.: doctor and patient were on excellent terms with each other, but the result had not been therapeutic.

Several months later Dr. Smith reported on Mrs. Lowe, whom she had seen again. In response to a question, the patient said that she was having intercourse only because the doctor had ordered her to. Mother used to order her about, and she said that she used to do everything mother ordered. Dr. Smith asked her what her feelings were about her husband's body; did she look at him? Mrs. Lowe replied, 'Oh, I couldn't!' She had seen a little boy's penis; 'That was soft and sweet. But don't ask me to talk about my husband's—I shall be sick if I do.' At this point the patient retched quite a lot and the doctor did not pursue the topic further. When asked why she had married her husband, the patient said he had been having an *affaire* with a woman ten years older and she had taken him away from her. Just before they were married he had told her that he had lived with an Oriental woman. Every time they attempted intercourse she thought of this woman being better than herself.

At the next visit there was another good post-coital test. Dr. Smith asked her whether she was now having intercourse for her husband's sake. The patient said that she was getting on much better and was beginning to enjoy it. She could now tolerate the back view of her husband's body but not the front.

DISCUSSION

SMITH

She said she was still angry with me because I was making such a fuss about intercourse and not bothering about the baby. I said we would arrange an appointment with a gynaecologist for a tubal insufflation. She was frightened and said, 'I will go if you will come with me and hold my hand.' I said, 'Don't you think it's time you stood on your own feet without Mummy's help?'

BALINT

I want to stress the fact that it is possible for you to work just as well with an angry relationship as with a friendly co-operative one. This teaches us that you don't need to be excessively gentle, meek, and mild with your patients. You can be honest. But the woman's neurosis remains after consummation. She is still an angry woman with a lot of problems. One difficulty now is that Dr. Smith cannot get out of this ding-dong battle with the patient.

BAKER

Perhaps the patient is re-enacting her parent's battle with Dr. Smith.

SMITH

Sexually and physically father was the attacker in her view.

BALINT

She has encouraged you to play this role with her; you have to do to her what father did to mother. She is able to trigger off something in you so that you do this; it fits your temperament, and you even seem to enjoy it. This is what we call being seduced by the patient. Perhaps when she expressed her fear of the tubal insufflation it would have been more useful to her if you could have changed from an attacker to a sympathizer. This might have allowed her to express her fears more fully. Her relationship with you has many facets. It would be worth while to explore others of them.

The following month Dr. Smith reported again on Mrs. Lowe. When she had returned to see the doctor for the insufflation she had asked to speak to Dr. Smith. She looked very cheerful and said that she could face the procedure alone. She said she was now having intercourse 'for the baby and for my husband. I don't like it but I see I ought to accept it in the marriage, and my husband says I am getting to be more of a wife. I'm beginning not to need your orders.'

Dr. Smith reported:
After the session with the gynaecologist, Sister asked me to see Mrs. Lowe, who was in a flood of tears. She had been quite reasonable at first, but when he got to the uncomfortable part she started sobbing. She had the same effect on him she'd had on me—he went for her, although it wasn't like him to do that, and she reacted to the challenge by telling him to go on. In the middle of her tears she said to me, 'Men are useless. They don't understand women. You can, but mother never did. I don't feel angry with you now. You understand me, you saw through me. My father was a very sweet person but mother always ran him down. Mother said he got her pregnant out of spite. Now I hate my mother.'

At this point psychotherapy seemed to have stopped, and the patient's further treatment was left to the gynaecologist. The final report from Dr. Smith came a year later:

She had been attending the clinic regularly, but not on the days I am there, and was not yet pregnant. This time she came on my day and asked Sister if she could see me. No reason had been found for her difficulty in conceiving. She said she wasn't too worried about not being pregnant. Her relationship with her husband was much better, she said, and she enjoyed intercourse. She said, 'Do you remember when I tried to be sick when you talked about it? Do you know, if I met a woman who was as idiotic as I was, I could convince her that it was nice.'

97

I asked her what she thought had helped her. She said, 'I think it was just that you nagged at me. I thought, if this person is so persistent and so patient and so determined to see me again, it makes me feel that I am at least worth bothering about.' I thought that was quite interesting. She said, 'Strangely, I get on much better with my parents now. I felt there was a wall, and my parents were on the other side of it, and my husband was on the other side of it too. When I broke down the barrier with my husband, I suddenly made better contact with my parents.'

In the discussion it was pointed out that the doctor had treated this last session as a meeting of two old friends rather than a professional visit, and had thereby missed the opportunity to help the patient to examine what other feelings she may have had besides gratitude. It seemed that the patient was presenting an over-beautiful picture of her life and had idealized her relationship with the doctor. Dr. Smith then recalled some critical remarks the patient had made about other people during the session. She agreed that the pleasure she had felt at the patient's expression of gratitude had prevented her from seeing that the patient still had aggressive feelings towards her, which had been displaced onto other people.

This case material has been quoted at some length because it illustrates several points. Again we see the woman who is much more aggressive and controlling than she appears to be. For a variety of reasons—some circumstantial, some in the doctor's personality, and some in the patient's way of dealing with people—the doctor responded in an angry way, aggressively confronting the patient with what she was doing. An intense relationship developed rapidly which was only partially examined. It mirrored aspects of the patient's relationship with her mother as well as aspects of her parents' relationship with each other as she viewed it in her fantasy. In this case, the violation of the principle that the doctor's feelings should be examined rather than acted upon had some therapeutic result, but this should not be construed as a recommendation that doctors discharge their anger at patients whenever they feel like it. Because of the unusual degree of matching between the doctor's feelings and the patient's needs, the result was a fair degree of success after three previous doctors had failed, although the work remained incomplete.

There are hints in the material of areas of difficulty that were not interpreted. Throughout is the theme of her intense attachment to women, the implications of which were not explored. The extent to which loving and fighting were confused for her was not explicitly considered. Her aversion to looking at her husband's body was partially altered in that she could look at him from the back only; this suggests an unconscious wish to deny the difference between the sexes— from the back, men and women look more similar. Her conflicting feelings about parental intercourse during her childhood were incompletely explored. Her feelings of unworthiness suggest a degree of latent depression. A thorough resolution of her conflicts would require the exploration of these and other areas in the course of psychotherapy. A more neutral attitude on the part of the therapist might have facilitated their emergence in the transference in a form which permitted their full interpretation and resolution. The doctor here had a more limited goal, the consummation of the marriage with some amelioration of other marital problems, and, because of the clinic setting, a limited time in which to work. Although many problems remain unsolved, the method used was relatively successful where traditional medical techniques had failed.

The technique of 'doing a Smith' was adopted with variations by some of the other doctors in certain cases. It tended to work well with patients whose aggressiveness was not far below the surface but was hidden by a veneer of sweetness. Not all the doctors could use this technique even when they wanted to. The doctor must work within the limitations of flexibility in style which his own character imposes on him. To 'do a Smith', the doctor must be reasonably at home with his own aggressiveness and not too frightened of the patient's released aggressiveness.

Like any technique it can be misapplied. Dr. Smith herself found that it fails completely with patients who are quite overtly anxious or depressed, and only causes them to retreat further behind their defences. It also fails with the patient who is aggressive, angry, and demanding from the start, who often is covertly depressed. The doctor to whom this approach comes naturally must be careful that it is always used as a technique in the patient's interest, rather than as a discharge of the doctor's feelings.

On the basis of work with other patients, the seminar doctors consider that there are occasional indications for the doctor to choose to depart from a position of professional detachment by deliberately expressing positive feelings. Particularly with patients who are openly aggressive and demanding towards the doctor from the start, where this seems to be a protective covering over feelings of depression and worthlessness, it may be helpful if the doctor shows considerable warmth and sympathy towards the patient.

My own opinion is that consistent interpretation by the doctor is a far safer course in psychotherapy than any expression of his own feelings. Such expressions of emotion by the doctor are most apt to occur in response to provocative behaviour by the patient. In all likelihood this will result in the repetition of a familiar pattern in the patient's experience with other people. The unique experience the doctor can offer the patient when he preserves his professional attitude is the experience of having someone who understands what she is doing, accepts it for what it is, and helps the patient to understand it herself.

CHAPTER 7

Examining the Patient's Fantasies

The patient's fantasies are important determinants of her attitude to intercourse and to treatment designed to help her to consummate her marriage. First we will examine some of the fantasy meanings of certain physical techniques which have been recommended by gynaecologists for the treatment of non-consummation. If the doctor acts on the patient's wish for physical treatment, he may be assisting the patient to act out the fantasies that prompt the request rather than understanding them. In the course of case presentations, various fantasies women have about their bodies which interfere with a straightforward approach to intercourse are discussed. The last two cases illustrate the importance of recognizing and treating non-consummation when the patient initially presents some other complaint.

Throughout this case material, themes developed earlier reappear. Some of these patients show aspects of the Sleeping Beauty syndrome, others resemble Brunhild in some respects, while in others the wish for a baby without intercourse can be discerned. The importance of understanding the doctor's emotions is evident in several cases.

MRS. PARKER

One patient in this series, Mrs. Parker, a 26-year-old woman who had been married for 2½ years, was very fearful of pain in intercourse and requested the doctor to stretch her vagina under anaesthesia. The case was reported during the early months of the seminar. She seemed to be intensely attached to possessive parents who were prone to violent outbursts of anger. She was concerned about her parents' dislike of her husband's parents. Shortly after her engagement, her parents had turned her prospective husband out of the house because they were resentful at not having been invited to his sister's wedding.

Love play was enjoyable for her but she became panicky when her husband attempted to penetrate. Her husband was becoming impatient with her and they had angry scenes about it. He blamed her mother for all the difficulties and would not speak to her when she visited. The patient sided with her parents and was angry at the way her husband treated them. Her mother appeared from her description to be an excitable person who was the dominant figure in the family.

The doctor advised the patient, who had vaginismus but very little hymen, to stretch herself. She came back the second time saying she hadn't been able to accomplish much this way. This time the doctor did a more thorough examination and concluded that she had a fibrous band constricting the lower third of the vagina, preventing the insertion of two fingers. Under nitrous oxide gas anaesthesia, the patient showed no relaxation and the doctor had to work hard to stretch the vagina to admit three fingers.

After the procedure, the patient appeared much more relaxed. She said, 'Isn't gas lovely! I did enjoy it.' She inserted a series of dilators the doctor gave her but refused the offer to take them home, saying she would have intercourse. She telephoned the doctor a few days later to say that she had had intercourse and everything was going well.

In the discussion which followed this presentation, some doctors wondered whether there had indeed been a fibrous band or whether the findings were due to a muscular spasm which had not relaxed under the light anaesthesia produced by nitrous oxide. They then turned to speculating about the patient's unexpressed fantasy which had been acted out. One doctor remarked that the fantasy of being raped under gas was not uncommon. Others expanded on this idea: the patient was put on a couch half undressed, in anticipation that something would happen to her, put under an anaesthetic which she felt was 'lovely', and awoke with a sore feeling in her vagina to say, 'I did enjoy it.' All this taken together seemed very suggestive that her previous excessive fear of pain on intercourse was related to an unconscious wish that her first intercourse be a rape. In a way she had acted this out with the doctor so that she could be painlessly 'raped' by being stretched under gas anaesthesia. The doctor was criticized for not helping the patient to discuss her fantasies at the time, and urged to try to help her to understand herself better when she returned, but this she never did.

The use of dilators is another technique that has been recommended by various authors. Particularly towards the beginning of the seminar, some of the doctors occasionally used them. In discussing one case where the patient had refused to examine herself with her fingers but had no difficulty in inserting a dilator the doctor gave her, it became apparent that some doctors had strong feelings about the use of dilators as against fingers. As they discussed the topic, the doctors realized that part of the difficulty was that they and the patient might feel that the doctor was in a way encouraging the patient to masturbate, which aroused some guilt in both of them. The use of a dilator by the patient tended to disguise this, since it was less personal than using her fingers. They decided it was generally better to face the guilt that prevented the patient from using her fingers, when it was there, and help her to understand it for what it was.

Another patient expressed great fears of being damaged by her husband's penis. After she had been fitted with a cap she returned to say that she had not slept for three nights, she had been so frightened with the cap inside her. She had been afraid to move for fear it would disappear inside her so that she could not get hold of it again. Her fantasy was that her vagina was a hollow tube going straight into her abdomen into which things could disappear. She asked the doctor many questions about how far the penis would go into her when she had intercourse, and exactly what would happen to it. She remained fearful of intercourse after four interviews. In the fifth interview the doctor offered her some glass dilators which she took to at once, using them at home for a few days. Then she had intercourse, imagining when her husband first penetrated that he was putting a dilator into her. After this she was able to have intercourse and enjoy it without this fantasy. Apparently, in this case, the dilator was helpful. As soon as she could identify her husband's penis with the harmless dilator she had handled, she lost her fear of being damaged by it. Also, the experience of inserting the dilator and recovering it helped her to realize that her vagina was not a bottomless pit that would swallow things up, as she had imagined.

Another patient who was able to use dilators but resisted inserting her own fingers into her vagina finally expressed her fear that she might put her fingers in her rectum instead. In discussing her case, one doctor mentioned other patients who express a confusion between the vagina and the rectum. They feared using the toilet when they had a cap in, imagining that when their bowels open up, everything opens up. One doctor spoke of a patient who somehow managed to put her cap into her rectum every time, even when doing it under the doctor's supervision.

Another patient in the series objected strongly to using a dilator but was able to insert her finger in her vagina. She also showed considerable unconscious linking of her vagina and her rectum, which seemed related to extremely destructive fantasies. Here is her story in some detail.

MRS. WEISS

Mrs. Weiss was a 23-year-old woman whose marriage had been unconsummated for three years. She felt unable to have intercourse because she believed her vagina was very small and her husband's penis very large. Her own doctor, a man, had examined her and recommended a long series of repeated dilatations under anaesthesia; she had come to the clinic to seek a second opinion.

Her parents were happily married, she said; she got on well with mother and could discuss everything with her. An older married sister had told her that she didn't enjoy intercourse, although she hadn't had difficulty in consummating her marriage. She described her 28-year-old husband as very kind and considerate. They had enjoyed heavy petting during the year they had been engaged.

She had many boy friends before she became engaged and had difficulty restraining herself then during sex play, but always stopped short of intercourse because she thought it was wrong and was afraid of pregnancy. During her engagement she strongly desired intercourse, but as soon as she was married she didn't want it often. Her husband made one attempt at coitus on their honeymoon but she was frightened by the size of his penis and tightened up. Following that, he seldom tried; they satisfied each other with mutual masturbation.

Prior to the honeymoon she hadn't been frightened of her husband's penis. They had both read books on sex instruction but she could not apply what she read to herself. She expressed her fearful fantasy that her husband would rip her open if he tried to penetrate. Her thoughts turned from intercourse to the experience of having had an enema, which she found painful, after a tonsillectomy at the age of 12, and then to some painful injections she had for haemorrhoids four years previously. She was afraid that if she had intercourse her haemorrhoids would return.

During the pelvic examination she was tense but had only slight vaginismus. She had an intact hymen which stretched easily. During the examination she complained of pressure on her rectum, but was able to contract and relax her pelvic muscles. She strongly objected to a dilator but did not mind the doctor's examining finger. She feared she might harm herself by putting her own finger in, but was able to do so.

Following this initial presentation, Dr. Balint expressed his opinion that Mrs. Weiss would be a difficult patient to help by means of short-term techniques, and that referral to a psychiatrist should be kept in mind as a possibility. Unlike many of the other cases, whose neurotic inhibitions were on the surface, her problems seemed firmly embedded in her character.

Dr. Heath reported her findings after she had seen the patient a second time. The patient said she could insert two fingers into her vagina but not three. She didn't mind her husband inserting two fingers, but she was still afraid of his penis. During an attempt at intercourse she feared it would go right through her abdominal wall. Although she felt more relaxed, experienced more sexual feeling, and had more para-vaginal glandular secretions during sex play, she still couldn't permit penetration. She thought that she was less passionate than she had been during courtship. Dr. Heath told her that she was afraid of letting herself go; in the past she had been more able to do so because she knew she wouldn't permit herself to have intercourse.

Mrs. Weiss then said, 'My husband masturbates himself, doctor; do you think this is wrong? After he has been with me he goes out to wash himself and I think he does it then.' She seemed worried about this. Dr. Heath said she didn't think it would do him any harm; if he was worried about it, he could have an appointment to discuss it with a doctor. Mrs. Weiss did not think he would want to.

She was distressed because her non-consummation was upsetting her mother. She was very frightened of causing her mother any worry; she felt that she had always been the problem child of the family, and thought that she wasn't as good a daughter as her mother deserved. Then she said she was afraid of her piles returning.

The ensuing seminar discussion focused on the need for further exploration of her relationship to her mother, her aggressive fantasies about being torn open, and the guilt she felt at possibly harming her husband by causing him to masturbate. Her fear that her husband would rip her open may have been related to her guilt over what she felt she had done to her husband. Being ripped open would be her punishment for this. If she could be led towards a desire to comply and satisfy her husband instead of being aggressive towards him, perhaps she wouldn't be so afraid of what he might do to her. Her vagina and her rectum were very much confused

109

in her fantasy; perhaps she could experiment to find out what she felt in the two passages and whether she could discriminate between the different feelings.

The doctor presented a brief final report on Mrs. Weiss many months later which gave no indication that she had been able to discuss this material with the patient during two subsequent visits. During the first of these the patient complained of pain from an impacted wisdom tooth and a painful period she had that day, and said she wasn't getting on very well. The next time she spoke of how constipated she had been since her previous visit, and how she had had an attack of haemorrhoids. She failed to keep her fifth appointment. She wrote in reply to the doctor's follow-up letter that she was getting on all right; the visits to the clinic had helped, but she didn't want to come back again. It seemed unlikely that she had consummated her marriage.

We have previously considered the fact that a fear of intercourse as a painful attack may conceal the wish for it to be just this. In Mrs. Weiss' case, something else seems to be involved as well. In part her fear represents her expectation of what unconsciously seems a fitting punishment for her hidden destructive wishes towards her husband. Another aspect of it is a defence against acknowledging to herself the intensity of her aggression towards her husband; she admits to herself that intense aggressiveness is somehow involved in her view of intercourse, but projects it into her husband. As had been predicted, this patient's difficulties proved to be beyond the reach of the limited psychotherapeutic work which the seminar doctors are able to do. Part of the skill that must be developed in this work involves judging the limitations of the technique.

The working hypotheses of the seminar have been that this technique is most likely to be successful when the patient has had a good relationship with her mother, comes for help soon after marriage, takes a matter-of-fact attitude to the problem by facing it openly rather than coming on account of infertility or some other problem, and, when given the opportunity, expresses fear but little or no disgust. Marked disgust for her genitals or for intercourse have been taken as bad prognostic signs, but fear and anxiety have not. Later we will see how these working hypotheses stand up when the data on one hundred cases are systematically evaluated.

In a small number of cases in the series, the fact that consummation had not taken place was discovered incidentally when the woman consulted a doctor with another complaint unrelated to problems with intercourse or conception. Several others were discovered when the patient came requesting a cap.

MRS. OWEN

Mrs. Owen, a 32-year-old typist, first saw her family doctor with vague complaints of a 'bad back'. He asked her whether she was happily married, and she revealed that she had not had intercourse during her four years of marriage. The doctor found an intact hymen and severe vaginismus. He instructed her in muscle relaxation and tried gentle dilatation without avail, so he referred her to Dr. White.

She was an attractive young woman who was dressed very tidily and seemed shy at first. She told Dr. White that she enjoyed sex play but immediately became tense when her husband attempted intercourse.

She was the eldest girl, the second child in a large family. When she was seven her mother had had an operation and the patient was sent to stay with friends. During her stay there, the husband in the family came to her room one night and stroked her vulva. She wanted to scream but he told her not to and said that it didn't matter. She mentioned

111

this to no one during childhood, but later thought about it frequently and, on her marriage, told her husband as well as her family doctor. She thought this might be the reason for her difficulty in consummating.

Shortly after this incident, Mrs. Owen's parents separated. Her mother went to work and the patient enjoyed taking care of the younger children.

At 15 she left school and had worked ever since. She had had a number of casual boy friends but her husband was the first man she became seriously interested in. He was a butcher, three years younger than she was.

When Dr. White first saw her, the patient professed complete ignorance about her anatomy and Dr. White gave her factual explanations. The mild vaginismus she showed on examination soon relaxed. Mrs. Owen was able to examine herself at the doctor's suggestion without difficulty. The doctor advised her to stretch herself and gave her some lubricating jelly.

A fortnight later she returned to report no progress; she blamed this on her menstrual period, which started soon after her first visit. In this interview, Dr. White learned that the patient considered herself very unsociable and found it difficult to be other than highly inhibited with people except after she had had a drink. Mrs. Owen thought that she needed more stretching. When the doctor asked her how long she thought it would take, the patient quoted her family doctor as saying that it might take a year, and seemed to accept this calmly. The patient had forgotten her anatomy lesson and Dr. White went over it all again with her.

In the discussion following this presentation, Dr. White was criticized for trying to teach the patient rather than interpreting her defence of 'not knowing'. Other doctors then commented on the strong resistance against consummating which the patient hid behind a bland and superficially co-operative exterior.

Attention then shifted to the childhood trauma she had reported. Balint felt that long-term psychotherapy or psycho-analysis would be necessary to explore the many feelings and fantasies that were probably connected with this and its relationship in her mind to her mother's operation and subsequent separation from father. He suggested that Dr. White should avoid this area entirely, concentrating on her current resistance, attempting to find the aggressive trends in the patient which were being masked by the doctor's over-helpful approach. This might help her to consummate; after this, if she wanted further help with her deeper problems, she could be referred elsewhere.

In the next session, a more vivid picture of her mother and father emerged. Mother had come from a wealthy family and married so far beneath them that they had disowned her. She seemed to romanticize her discussion of mother's life and expressed considerable affection for her. Father tended to gamble away the money mother earned, and the patient's parents quarrelled frequently. The patient was father's favourite and enjoyed going for walks with him. She had strongly resented the fact that he had always taken away the presents she had received from her grandmother and had pawned or sold them.

During the interview the doctor noted that the patient passively accepted what the doctor said but seemed unmoved by it; Dr. White began to feel angry. She recognized this as a symptom of the patient's illness, and told the patient that she felt frustrated by her passive resistance and expected that she did the same thing to her husband. The patient agreed with this, smiling blandly. Dr. White then told Mrs. Owen that she had married her husband to

113

mother him and didn't want to be a wife to him at all. The patient's only response was a placid smile. Dr. White asked her how she could sit calmly and let her say such things without reacting; the patient said, 'I suppose I had it coming to me.'

Mrs. Owen returned a month later; nothing had changed. Dr. White told her in this interview that she was punishing her husband for the way her father had behaved, but this didn't seem to mean anything to the patient. When asked whether she would be jealous if her husband were to become interested in another woman and leave her, the patient replied that she did not think so. She said 'If that happened I couldn't say anything because I would have driven him to it.' Feeling defeated, Dr. White asked her to bring her husband next time.

The seminar felt that the patient tended to live in a world of fantasy; Dr. White added that the patient's main leisure interest was reading women's magazines. Balint thought that the question of jealousy was not an appropriate one to raise with this patient; she seemed too immature to experience this emotion. It appeared that she mostly wanted to be mothered by her husband; if he were to leave her she might feel sorry and lonely rather than jealous.

Mr. Owen arrived alone to see Dr. White at the next appointment. He said that they had been afraid to come together lest he say such annoying things that they would quarrel when they got home. His main complaints were that his wife was a cold person who never showed him any affection. He felt she was too much tied to her mother, who had supper with them almost every night. His wife would often be so absorbed in conversation with her mother that she would ignore him. At times he wanted to knock their

114

heads together and storm out of the house. Before they were married his wife had been very gay and lively at parties, but now she hardly spoke to people. She always postponed love-making with a variety of excuses. He spoke about all this with a smile, scarcely showing any feeling.

The next time they came together. Mrs. Owen looked very attractive in new clothes and a new coiffure. Dr. White described the interview as non-productive. At one point Dr. White said that Mrs. Owen didn't want to be a wife and asked Mr. Owen whether he got angry at her. He said, 'Yes, sometimes I want to hit her.' Mrs. Owen said that he had done so. He denied it, saying that he had only pushed her away; she agreed with this. It appeared that they had quarrels in bed after she refused to have intercourse. She became aggressively silent at such times, which exasperated him. Her husband said she was more relaxed after a few drinks, but then he didn't want intercourse; he wanted her to be willing without drink.

In the discussion one doctor wondered whether part of the difficulty was that she might wish to be swept off her feet, and this would be in conflict with his wish for a consenting woman. The patient still had not accepted the aggressiveness in her passivity. Both partners seemed afraid of intense expressions of emotion. As the complexities of the case had become more apparent, it now seemed that moderately long-term treatment would be necessary.

At the date of writing this chapter (May 1961) treatment is continuing, but as yet the marriage has not been consummated.

MRS. CRISP

The next case is that of a patient who sought help indirectly by coming to the F.P.A. clinic for a cap; during the interview she revealed that her marriage had not been consummated. She was one of the patients who suffered from intense disgust for sexuality.

Dr. Monroe saw Mrs. Crisp after she had been seen twice by another woman doctor, not a member of the seminar, who had found that the patient had severe vaginismus and became nauseated during the pelvic examination. Attempts to encourage the patient to stretch herself had made her agitated and tearful. She was then referred to Dr. Monroe.

Mrs. Crisp was a 29-year-old office worker, who had been married for four months to a 31-year-old man, whom she had met at work. She had never had boy friends before. They married after 9 months of courtship. She said that she had a strong aversion from any form of love-making, which had become so much worse since her marriage that she now felt sick if her husband even put his arm around her. She volunteered very little in the interview and Dr. Monroe had to be very active in encouraging her to talk.

With great difficulty the patient spontaneously remarked that it was the idea that she might enjoy intercourse that shocked her most. She had always been horrified that people might enjoy it. She knew that it was necessary in order to have a child but wished it could be over instantaneously. The closest she could get to expressing her feelings about it was to say that she disliked the thought of being mauled about.

Sex had never been mentioned in her household; the subject was taboo. When her menstrual periods began she disliked them intensely, cried, and stayed in bed all day. Mother apparently had accepted this as a natural reaction, and they never discussed it. She described her father as 'spoiled'; when asked to explain this further, she only said

116

that he had refused to have another child when mother wanted one.

Mrs. Crisp said that she thought her husband was wonderful and that she loved him very much. Dr. Monroe said that she probably wanted to put things right so that she could enjoy this aspect of marriage. The patient replied, 'Oh no, I don't want to like it.' She said that she did not wish her marriage to break up but she wanted no kind of sexual feeling. She denied any knowledge of sex and said that she never thought of such things as a child or a young woman.

After the first presentation of this case, the group agreed that the doctor's main task was to confront the patient with her hatred of being a woman and her attempts completely to deny her femininity. Because of her strong disgust, the prognosis was considered poor.

In the next interview the patient started by saying, 'I know I am at fault but it is difficult to correct it. I suppose it is fear of the unknown. That must be one of the reasons for having a honeymoon.' It then transpired that they were married in a Registry Office and afterwards she did some week-end shopping with her husband. They had no honeymoon. They married earlier than they had intended to because a flat had become available and it was very sparsely furnished. She spent the week-end cleaning the kitchen unit. The idea of a wedding dress had seemed repugnant to her. 'Money is far better spent on a good suit.'

Dr. Monroe commented that she had difficulty in being a woman and in seeing herself as a woman. The patient said, 'I always felt there was something wrong with me because I never had any boy friends.' Then she went back to the wedding dress: 'When you are past 25 you are too old

117

to get away with it.' Dr. Monroe said that she seemed to dislike the idea of allowing herself any pleasure. The patient replied, 'I like eating. I have very strong likes and dislikes.' With intense feeling she said, 'I hate having periods. I once told my mother I wished I could have the whole bag of tricks removed.'

At this point the interview changed; the patient leaned forward and began to talk rapidly in an excited way about her periods. 'Of course I never have a bath during my period. Is it all right to wash your hair? Mother said not to, but I did once and I didn't have any pain. Is it all right to use Tampax? Mother said no. I don't know what a period is. I have read it is the egg getting ready in case it fertilized.'

Dr. Monroe talked a bit about physiology with her while the patient listened eagerly. The patient said she wanted to use Tampax and Dr. Monroe told her what to do. She then said she wanted to be fitted with a cap. The doctor told her she would do this on her next visit.

The seminar doctors commented on the primacy of her relationship with her mother in the material; husband and father scarcely emerged as people in her account. The advisability of teaching physiology to her was questioned. Dr. Monroe replied that this had been minimal; she had hoped that the patient might move from the topic of menstruation to a discussion of her fantasies about intercourse. Some doctors thought that the patient should have been examined at the time she requested it. Postponing examination might lead to increased resistance next time. The dramatic change in the patient from one interview to the other was partly related to a change in the way the doctor had dealt with her. At first the doctor had been a bit taken aback and had been somewhat withdrawn, as the patient had been. The second time the doctor had been more forthcoming, and the patient was able to reveal some of her concerns.

The next time the patient came she spoke of the difficult journey she had had. She hadn't been feeling well that day and her husband told her not to come. The knowledge that she would be examined this time frightened her. In preparing for the examination she said she wished she had never married, because this was sure to hurt. After considerable initial difficulty, the examination was accomplished without undue distress to the patient, and she managed to examine herself. A cap was then fitted and she was pleased at how easily she learned how to use it.

Next time she arrived as instructed with the cap properly in place, feeling triumphant at mastering the cap technique. She lived some distance from London and said that it would be more convenient to go to a local clinic for her follow-up visits. Later Dr. Monroe wrote a letter requesting follow-up information but received no reply; the question of consummation in this case unfortunately remains indeterminate.

It seems as if psychotherapy stopped in these last two interviews. Doctor and patient colluded in shifting the emphasis to cap technique and away from the patient's guilt and repugnance about sexuality. Something had been achieved since the patient reacted quite differently from the way she had to her previous examination, but many questions remained unanswered.

The cases presented in this chapter conclude our sampling of the variety of clinical material present in the series of one hundred cases which have been studied. The next chapter contains a number of facts about the series as a whole.

CHAPTER 8

The Findings in One Hundred Cases

This chapter presents data collected during the study and treatment of one hundred cases of unconsummated marriage. The work presented here properly belongs to the exploratory phases of research, in which new territory is traversed, its general features noted, and the boundaries roughly marked out. The hypotheses generated in the course of this work need further testing. Like many early maps of a new region, it will doubtless be found faulty in some respects when the territory is systematically surveyed.

The results must be evaluated in the context of the work. The primary aim was the practical one of developing new therapeutic techniques to help patients consummate their marriages. In interviewing their patients, the doctors never followed a systematic course of inquiring into, say, family background, or any other particular area; indeed, they were encouraged to follow the patient's material wherever it led. Therefore there are many gaps in the data. Reports on patients to the seminar varied from short paragraphs in the transcript to many pages; inevitably they were highly condensed reports of what had happened, each doctor reporting what seemed significant to her.

To organize these data, I prepared a worksheet covering a number of points which seemed of interest, such as the length of the period of non-consummation at the first visit, the presenting complaint, the number of treatment sessions before consummation, the findings on pelvic examination, the patient's reaction to examination, the husband's potency, the patient's attitude towards sex pre-maritally, and so on. Each item was subdivided into variable numbers of categories. For example, the checklist item 'presenting complaint' had four subgroups: 'Non-consummation, infertility, request for cap, other complaint'. Under the heading 'vaginismus', the ratings were: 'absent, slight, moderate, severe, not mentioned'. The item 'patient's motivation for consummation' was subdivided: 'apparently eager, indifferent, secondary to the wish for a baby, pressure from husband, pressure from families, pressure from others, undetermined'.

Using this checklist, the transcripts of the one hundred case reports were evaluated and each patient was scored on each item. The data were then transferred to punched cards to facilitate tabulation of results and evaluation of the effect of various findings on outcome. There are many possible sources of error in this method. To mention a few, the reporting doctors probably differed to some extent in their evaluation of the degrees of vaginismus or the patient's motivation for consummation. In some items, the rater had to evaluate the report of the doctor, as in scoring the apparent overall degree of emotional disturbance in the patient. Perhaps another rater might have come to somewhat different conclusions. Again, it must be emphasized that this is exploratory research. The method of evaluating the reports seemed consistent with the degree of precision with which the primary data had been collected, that is, the level of accuracy is that of clinical reporting rather than controlled experimentation.

With this in mind, only the most limited statistical operations on the data seemed appropriate. The sample is not a random one. To test the statistical significance of observed differences of outcome between subgroups of patients in the series, the χ^2 test[1] was used (Hill, 1949). The use of this test requires no assumptions about randomness in the sample. What is meant by statistical significance? This is best illustrated by an example.

Suppose that 17 out of 27 patients (63 per cent), all of whom showed a given finding (e.g. motivation for consummation judged to be secondary to the wish for a baby), consummated their marriages after treatment, whereas 54 out of 61 patients (89 per cent) who did not show this finding consummated. The question arises, is this difference in outcome between the two groups a real one? Is the prognosis poorer when the patient shows this finding, or is the apparent difference due to chance factors operating in a small sample? To put it another way, the question is, if very large numbers of patients were evaluated, is this apparent difference likely to remain or will it turn out to be spurious? This likelihood can be evaluated as a probability that there is no real difference between the two groups: that the apparent difference is due to chance. A difference is said to be statistically significant when the probability of no real difference is lower than some arbitrary value, usually taken as 5 chances in 100 ('significant at the 0.05 level'). This means that if the results are repeatedly investigated using very large numbers of patients, the odds are about 20 to 1 that some difference in outcome will be found between the two groups. It must be stressed that the χ^2 test gives no information about the *degree* of the difference between the two groups, merely the probability that *some* real difference exists.

[1] The tests were all conducted as fourfold tables (one degree of freedom), applying in all cases Yates's correction for continuity.

Virgin Wives

With this in mind, we now turn to the actual results and findings. Outcome was divided into six categories: non-consummation; technical consummation (complete intercourse once or more times, but apparently not regularly accepted as a part of married life); regular intercourse with orgasm; regular intercourse with frigidity; regular intercourse, but the question of pleasure experienced by the woman cannot be evaluated from the case report (tabulated as 'regular intercourse, ? pleasure'); and finally a category of patients who were lost to follow-up so that the outcome could not be determined. These results are shown in *Table* 1.

TABLE 1   OUTCOME AFTER TREATMENT

Outcome	*Number of patients*
Non-consummation	17
Unknown	12
Regular intercourse, orgasm	20
Regular intercourse, ? pleasure	36
Regular intercourse, frigid	5
Technical consummation	10
Total	100

There is no way of guessing the probable outcome in the 'unknown' category. Even if these are all taken as non-consummations (which seems unlikely), 71 out of 100 patients consummated their marriages. No claim is made that this means that the patients' marital conflicts had been fully resolved. Many problems clearly remain for them. The seminar doctors believe that consummation is a useful measure of the success of their treatment in keeping with the explicitly limited goals they tried to achieve. If the results are expressed in terms of the 88 patients for whom the outcome was known, 81 per cent consummated their marriages. The follow-up period varied widely, from weeks to years, generally limited to an interval of several weeks to several months.

Noteworthy in *Table* 1 is the observation that 20 patients experienced orgasm after they began to have intercourse. One might think that the patient who has not consummated her marriage represents an extreme example of frigidity, but this does not appear to be the case. Frigidity appears to represent a much more deep-seated problem requiring different techniques in treatment from those used in this series.

Of the hundred patients, 26 are known to have become pregnant. Their patterns of sexual intercourse after they knew they were pregnant are given in *Table* 2; the two non-consummated patients became pregnant by means of AIH.

TABLE 2   SEXUAL BEHAVIOUR AFTER
PREGNANCY ESTABLISHED

Outcome	Number of patients
Non-consummation	2
Frequency of intercourse unknown	7
Regular intercourse, orgasm	5
Regular intercourse, ? pleasure	9
Regular intercourse, frigid	1
Technical consummation	2
Total	26

The patients ranged in age (at the time of the first interview) from 18 to 54. The average age was 27. The distribution of ages is tabulated with the outcome for each age group in *Table* 3. Age does not appear to be significantly related to outcome.

TABLE 3   RELATIONSHIP OF PATIENT'S AGE TO
OUTCOME

Age at first interview	Total number	Non-consum-mation	Outcome Consum-mation	Unknown
Under 20	5	1	2	2
20–25	35	7	24	4
26–30	35	5	27	3
31–35	18	4	11	3
36–40	5	0	5	0
41–45 (41)	1	0	1	0
Over 45 (54)	1	0	1	0
Totals	100	17	71	12

The length of time the marriage had been unconsummated at the time of the first interview is tabulated with the outcome for each time interval in *Table* 4.

TABLE 4   RELATIONSHIP OF DURATION OF
NON-CONSUMMATION TO OUTCOME

Duration of non-consummation	Total Number	Non-consum-mation	Outcome Consum-mation	Unknown
Less than 1 month	7	1	6	0
1–3 months	11	0	9	2
3–6 months	10	2	5	3
6–12 months	7	1	6	0
1–1½ years	7	0	6	1
1½–2 years	6	0	6	0
2–3 years	9	5	4	0
3–4 years	6	2	2	2
4–5 years	9	4	5	0
5–7½ years	14	1	11	2
7½–10 years	11	1	9	1
More than 10 years (13, 14, 17)	3	0	2	1
Totals	100	17	71	12

Combining adjacent intervals within *Table* 4, we note the curious distribution shown in *Table* 5.

TABLE 5   RELATIONSHIP OF DURATION OF
NON-CONSUMMATION TO OUTCOME
(Cases of known outcome only)

Duration in years	Total Number	Non-consummation Number	Consummation Number	Per Cent
Up to and including 2	42	4	38	90%
2–5	22	11	11	50% } 72%
Over 5	24	2	22	92%

In general, one might expect the prognosis to be better the sooner treatment starts. This appears to be true for durations up to 2 years, but then the trend seems to reverse. Those cases of more than five years' duration appear to have the same prognosis as those of up to 2 years' duration. Comparing the group of up to 2 years' duration with the rest of the sample, the difference almost reaches the 0.05 level of significance ($x^2=3.81$; for $p=0.05$, $x^2=3.84$). The over-5-year group compared to the rest of the sample falls far short of a statistically significant difference ($x^2=1.90$). However, if the 2–5-year group is compared to the rest of the sample, the difference is statistically significant at far better than the 0.01 level. Indeed, 65 per cent of the failures among the 88 patients where the outcome of treatment is known occur among these 22 patients. Whatever the factor responsible for this poor result in the 2–5 year group, it is not a factor related to length of non-consummation alone, since it seems absent in the over-5-year group. An explanation for this observation will be offered later in this section when motivation is related to outcome. In any case it is apparent that treatment has been

127

successful in a high proportion of cases even when the non-consummation has been of long duration.

The distribution of age at marriage for the series is given in *Table* 6. This has no apparent prognostic effect.

TABLE 6   RELATIONSHIP OF AGE AT MARRIAGE TO OUTCOME

| | | Outcome | | |
Age at Marriage	*Total*	*Non-consum-mation*	*Consum-mation*	*Unknown*
Under 20	14	2	8	4
20–25	63	12	45	6
26–30	14	3	9	2
31–35	6	0	6	0
36–40	2	0	2	0
Over 40 (54)	1	0	1	0
Total	100	17	71	12

The difference in age between husband and wife was not a prognostic factor. Those patients whose husbands were younger than they were did not differ significantly in outcome from the rest.

One working hypothesis was that non-consummation could be successfully treated by working with the wife alone, although the presence of a collusive pattern between the spouses was recognized. In 28 cases, the husband was also seen, usually for a few minutes, sometimes for a full session alone or together with his wife. Of these cases, 23 consummated, 3 were unconsummated after treatment, and in 2 the outcome was unknown. Of the 72 cases where the wife alone was seen, 48 consummated, 14 remained unconsummated, and in 10 cases the outcome was unknown. The apparent trend in favour of those cases in which the husband was seen is without statistical significance.

Even more surprising is the finding that the husband's potency (assessed from the wife's report at the start of treatment) shows no relationship to outcome. The figures are given in *Table* 7. The difference in outcome between those cases in which the husband's potency was apparently normal and those in which it was impaired to some degree is not statistically significant.

TABLE 7 RELATIONSHIP OF HUSBAND'S POTENCY TO OUTCOME

Husband's potency	Total	Non-consum-mation	Consum-mation	Unknown
			Outcome	
Apparently normal	49	7	37	5
Sometimes impotent	13	2	10	1
Usually impotent	9	3	5	1
Secondary impotence	13	3	10	0
Not mentioned	16	2	9	5
Total	100	17	71	12

It is of interest that some degree of potency disturbance was initially present in at least 35 cases; in 13, the husband had initially been potent, but with the persistence of non-consummation had developed some degree of secondary impotence.

Of the 71 patients who consummated their marriages, all but 3 (96 per cent) did so after 5 or fewer sessions of treatment. These data are shown in *Table* 8.

TABLE 8 NUMBER OF TREATMENT SESSIONS PRIOR TO CONSUMMATION

Number of sessions	1	2	3	4	5	6–10	
Number of patients	28	18	8	6	8	3	Total 71

Virgin Wives

Considering the whole series of 100, 74 patients were seen a total of 1–5 times, 13 patients were seen 6–10 times, and 3 patients 10–15 times; none was seen more than 15 times. These data suggest that, with the technique employed, if the patient has not consummated her marriage after 5 sessions, she is not likely to benefit from further sessions of this sort.

Outcome showed no significant relationship to presenting complaint. Most patients came complaining of non-consummation directly. Of the rest, all but 10 complained of infertility. (One patient had had extensive investigations for infertility at another clinic before the fact of non-consummation was elicited!) The relationship of complaint to outcome is given in *Table* 9.

TABLE 9 RELATIONSHIP OF COMPLAINT TO OUTCOME

Presenting complaint	Total	Non-consummation	Outcome Consummation	Unknown
Non-consummation	72	10	51	11
Infertility	18	4	13	1
Cap request	6	2	4	0
Other complaint	4	1	3	0

Pelvic examination findings were reported on 92 cases. In 46 cases, the hymen was found to be intact. Vaginismus was absent in 42 cases, slight in 10, moderate in 15, severe in 19; in 14 cases its presence or absence could not be assessed from the case report. Neither the presence of vaginismus nor that of an intact hymen had any statistically significant relationship to outcome.

Organic pathology was found on examination in 6 cases. Of these, in 2 cases of vaginitis and 2 cases of cervical polyp, the pathology was clearly an incidental finding. One patient

130

had a large uterine fibroid but did not consummate after myomectomy; after convalescence from her operation, she consummated after brief psychotherapy. Another patient had a fibrous band in the lower third of her vagina which was stretched under anaesthesia, after which she consummated. Of these 6 cases, 4 consummated after treatment, 1 did not, and in 1 the outcome was unknown.

The patient's reaction to pelvic examination and to self-examination was classified as either matter-of-fact, anxious, shameful, disgusted, resistant, examination refused, or reaction not mentioned, for those cases in which these procedures were performed. Self-examination was performed in 90 cases, but the reaction of the patient was not reported in 23 of these. Of these reactions, only one showed a marked relationship to outcome. Of those patients who reacted with shame or disgust to pelvic examination, 4 out of 5 failed to consummate; 4 out of 9 patients who showed shame or disgust during self-examination failed to consummate. Of 32 patients whose reaction to examination was matter-of-fact, 5 failed to consummate. Only 2 out of 24 patients who showed a matter-of-fact reaction to self-examination failed to consummate. The number of patients showing shame or disgust during either of these procedures is too small to permit statistical evaluation, but the data strongly suggest that this is a poor prognostic sign. Similarly, when the patients were grouped on the basis of their reports of mother's attitude towards sex, the expression of disgust by the patient's mother seemed to be a poor prognostic factor; of 9 such cases, 3 patients consummated, 4 did not, and in 2 cases the outcome was unknown. Of 6 patients who themselves expressed attitudes of disgust about sexual intercourse, 3 consummated and 3 did not. Taken together, it would seem that disgust about sexuality indicates that treatment of this type is less likely to be successful in consummating the marriage.

K

Thirty-seven patients in the series had had previous unsuccessful treatment of some sort for their non-consummation; of these, 22 consummated, 12 did not, and in 3 cases the outcome was unknown. Of the 63 patients who had not had previous treatment, 49 consummated, 5 did not, and in 9 cases the outcome was unknown. This difference is statistically significant at better than the 0.01 level; the probability is less than 1 in 100 of it occurring by chance. It is to be expected that those who had already been treated unsuccessfully would have a worse prognosis. What is noteworthy is the fact that almost 60 per cent of this group were helped to consummate despite the failure of previous methods of treatment. Types of previous treatment included surgery in 12 cases, the use of dilators by a doctor in 9 cases, the use of dilators by the patient in 5 cases, and advice or reassurance by a doctor in 17 cases (some patients had had more than one type of treatment). Seven patients in the series had previously had some form of brief psychotherapy since they had been married, but it is not known whether they had mentioned this problem to the previous therapist.

An attempt was made to evaluate the patient's motivation for consummation on the basis of the first interview as reported. Of the categories examined, only one showed a statistically significant relationship to outcome. In 30 cases, the wish for a baby appeared to be much more prominent than the wish to consummate *per se*; of these, 17 consummated, 10 did not, and the outcome was unknown in 3 cases. The difference between the outcome in this group and the rest of the series was significant at better than the 0.05 level. Of course many of the other patients desired pregnancy as well, but this was not their main reason for coming for help.

When we considered the relationship between duration of non-consummation and success of treatment (*Table* 5), a curious observation was the lower proportion of successes in the 2-5-year group than in the over-5-year group. If we now re-examine this in the light of motivational factors it is possible to explain this observation. *Table* 10 contains the data of *Table* 5, with the addition in parentheses of the number of patients in each category whose primary motivation appeared to be the wish for a baby.

TABLE 10   RELATIONSHIP TO OUTCOME OF DURATION
OF NON-CONSUMMATION[1] AND WISH FOR A BABY[2]
(cases of known outcome only)

		Outcome		
Duration in years	Total Number	Non-consummation Number	Consummation Number	Per cent
Up to and including 2	42 *(7)*	4 *(0)*	38 *(7)*	90%
2-5	22 *(12)*	11 *(8)*	11 *(4)*	50% }72%
Over 5	24 *(8)*	2 *(2)*	22 *(6)*	92%

[1] Roman figures.   [2] Italic figures.

Inspection of these figures suggests that the poor percentage of success in the 2-5-year group may be related to the disproportionate number of patients in it whose wish for a baby was their primary motivation for treatment, a poor prognostic factor in itself. Indeed, almost all of the treatment failures among those patients who waited more than two years before coming for treatment were in cases where the wish for a baby was paramount. Perhaps both the length of time before coming for treatment and the primacy of the wish for a baby are somewhat different measures of poor motivation. Another possible interpretation is that the apparent primacy of the wish for a baby is a sign of poor prognosis only in patients who wait more than two years before seeking treatment.

The patient gave some account of her husband's attitude

133

towards the non-consummation in 61 cases. In 34 of these, the husband appeared to the wife to be indifferent about it, again showing the collusion which exists between the couple to maintain the *status quo*. No significant prognostic factors were found by comparing the reported attitude of the husband with outcome.

Several previous authors have commented that a high proportion of women whose marriages are unconsummated describe their husbands as kind and considerate, while other authors have suggested that the husbands are often described as over-aggressive. The patient's view of her husband could be evaluated in 59 cases for these attitudes; 47 patients described their husbands as kind and considerate, 1 as over-aggressive, and 11 mentioned other attributes suggesting passivity. Although a high proportion of husbands in this series were characterized as kind and considerate, passive rather than over-aggressive, this trait had no prognostic significance.

The patient's attitude towards pre-marital sex play could be evaluated in 40 cases. Of these, 23 said they had enjoyed it, 4 had tolerated it to some extent without much feeling, 5 had permitted some but felt very guilty about it, and 8 patients denied any such experience. These attitudes showed no differential effect on outcome.

Attitudes towards menstruation could be evaluated in 19 cases; of these, 11 experienced considerable pain during menstrual periods or otherwise connected menstruation with suffering. Five of these patients (45 per cent) consummated, 5 did not, and the outcome in 1 case was unknown. Dysmenorrhea is thus a sign of poor prognosis. The difference of outcome between this group and the rest of the sample is statistically significant at better than the 0.05 level.

Sexual traumas occurring in childhood have been mentioned by some authors as a cause of later non-consummation. The findings in this series do not confirm this view. Eight patients out of 100 mentioned sexual experiences with an adult during their childhood, either the touching of their genitals by an adult or exhibitionism by an adult. Of these, 5 consummated, 2 did not, and the outcome was unknown in 1 case. Even in these few cases the report of actual trauma must be considered with reservations, since such reports may be based on fantasy.

Childhood separation from mother, father, or both parents was mentioned by 26 patients (since information on this was not specifically sought by the doctors, the incidence may well be higher). It must be recalled that most patients in the series are of such an age as to have gone through the war years during childhood. Separation from mother, from father, or from both parents had no differential prognostic effect.

The patient's relationship with her mother was difficult to evaluate from the data; enough material to permit even a crude rating was present in less than half of the case reports. In general the seminar doctors had the impression that those patients who had relatively good relationships with their mothers had a somewhat better prognosis, but I was unable to evaluate this impression from the transcript of the case reports.

Fifty-four patients made some reported comment about their mothers' attitudes towards sex. Of these, 27 said the subject was never discussed, 10 described their mothers' attitudes towards sexuality as forbidding, 8 reported a matter-of-fact attitude, and 9 reported expressions of disgust towards sexuality. Of these, only disgust (as mentioned above) was significantly related to prognosis, the outcome being less favourable in those cases.

Data were too scanty to permit evaluation of the patient's relationship with father in most cases. The patient's view of her parents' relationship with each other was also rarely mentioned. In 6 cases, the patient's mother had complained to her about her own sex life; 3 of the patients who reported this consummated, 3 did not.

Using the doctor's reports, I made an attempt to rate the degree of psychiatric illness in the patient. In more than half the cases reported, no estimate of the degree of illness was possible; for those who could be rated, no prognostic trends emerged. The data were insufficient to permit assigning patients to the usual psychiatric categories.

Some physical method was used as well as psychotherapy in the treatment of 65 patients. The most frequently used method was that of teaching the patient to stretch herself with her hand. Fourteen patients were fitted with caps. Occasionally dilators were used by the doctor or by the patient. One patient was manually stretched under anaesthesia. Hymenectomy was never performed. No statistically significant difference in outcome was found between the 65 patients who had some physical treatment in addition to psychotherapy and those 35 who had only psychotherapy (nearly all had physical examinations). The results are given in *Table* 11.

TABLE 11   RELATIONSHIP OF OUTCOME TO PHYSICAL TREATMENT

Physical treatment used	Total	Non-consum-mation	Outcome Consum-mation	Unknown
Yes	65	12	48	5
No	35	5	23	7

Since almost all of the patients had had pelvic examinations, no separate assessment of their effect on outcome was possible. As has been previously mentioned, the seminar doctors believe that the performance of a pelvic examination by the doctor who does the psychotherapy, and encouragement of the patient to examine herself in the doctor's presence, are central elements of the technique they use.

The importance of the patient's sexual fantasies has been emphasized earlier in this book. Some fantasy was mentioned by 56 patients, 11 of whom expressed more than one. The fear of being damaged by the penis during intercourse was expressed by 12 patients. One patient feared damaging her husband's penis during intercourse. The fantasy that their vaginas were too small was expressed by 17 patients. Three patients expressed their ideas of disproportion in terms of the belief that husband's penis was too large. Eleven patients spoke of fearful ideas about pregnancy or delivery; of these, one feared that she would not relax enough at delivery to let the baby out, and another feared that she would develop an ectopic pregnancy if her husband's semen 'went in the wrong place'. Three patients expressed horror at the idea of 'something going inside'. Three patients spoke of a fear of smothering during intercourse. Two patients were afraid that the penis would enter the rectum. Six patients spoke of coitus as a disgusting act. One patient expressed her fear that the semen would be cold. No specific fantasy expressed by the patient showed a statistically significant relationship with outcome, although the expression of disgust might turn out to be a sign of poor prognosis if a larger series were studied (of 6 patients, 3 consummated, 3 did not).

Patients who spontaneously expressed the fantasies mentioned above during the course of a few interviews presumably did so because they were under considerable pressure of anxiety from them. Forty-four patients did not mention fantasies about intercourse during their interviews. This does not necessarily mean that they did not have fantasies. Possibly they did but were not under enough pressure from them to speak of them, or perhaps were unable to speak of them for some other reason. The atmosphere that exists during the treatment developed by the seminar doctors encourages the expression of fantasy, but of course to a lesser extent than does long-term psychotherapy or psychoanalysis. In the setting of this type of treatment, those patients who express no fantasies have a better prognosis than those who do, presumably because they are less intensely anxious about intercourse to start with. Of 44 patients who mentioned no fantasies, 38 consummated, 1 did not, and the outcome was unknown in 5 cases. Of 56 patients who expressed one fantasy or more, 33 consummated, 16 did not, and the outcome was unknown in 7 cases. This difference is statistically significant at better than the 0.01 level. Similarly, those who express multiple fantasies appear to have a worse prognosis than those who express one or none; of the 11 patients who expressed multiple fantasies, 6 consummated and 5 did not. The difference between the outcome in this group compared to the rest of the series is statistically significant at better than the 0.05 level. It appears that the prognosis is poorer the higher the intensity of fantasy activity in the patient, as measured by the expression of fantasy material in this type of treatment. This should not be interpreted as suggesting that the expression of fantasy by the patient should be discouraged; the opposite is the case. Treatment involves helping the patient to express her unrealistic fantasies so that they cease to be such strong barriers against sexual intercourse. When they are expressed and discussed openly, the patient is better able to recognize them as unrealistic, thereby ceasing to be inhibited by them.

A final item of information concerns the functioning of the training seminar itself. I evaluated the discussions following each case presentation in terms of the source of the clarification obtained by the presenting doctor from the discussion. In 52 cases, the primary source of new insight into the case was the seminar leader. In 2 instances, the presenting doctor herself spontaneously saw the material in a new light by virtue of presenting it. On 28 occasions, other doctors in the seminar provided the main clarifying comments. Eighteen cases were reported for the first time after successful treatment had been completed because they illustrated some point of interest.

SUMMARY

Summarizing the results reported in this chapter, 71 patients of 100 (81 per cent of those with known outcome) consummated their marriages, 96 per cent of them after 5 or fewer sessions. Orgasm or its absence after consummation was mentioned in 25 case reports; of these, 20 patients experienced orgasm. Non-consummation thus appears to be a condition that is different from frigidity rather than one that represents an extreme degree of frigidity. The average age of patients at the first interview was 27, 70 patients falling in the 20–30 age group; prognosis was unrelated to age, age at marriage, or age difference between spouses. The non-consummation had existed for 2 years or less in 42 cases, between 2 and 5 years in 22 cases (these had an especially poor prognosis), and more than 5 years in 24 cases. Early treatment seems to result in a slightly better prognosis, but a high proportion of cases of long duration were helped to consummate.

In at least 35 cases, the husbands were impotent to some degree when the wife came for treatment. However, the reported potency of the husband had no statistically significant relationship to outcome. Although the presence of a collusive pattern between the spouses in unconsummated marriages is recognized, treatment of the wife alone is apparently sufficient to lead to consummation in a high proportion of cases. Whether or not the husband is seen by the doctor treating the wife has no significant relationship to outcome.

In only 2 cases was organic pathology found which bore

any relationship to the non-consummation; in one and possibly both of these cases, psychological factors seemed more important. The prognosis was not significantly different for those patients having an intact hymen or vaginismus.

Treatment was successful in almost 60 per cent of cases who had had unsuccessful treatment of other sorts, although the prognosis was significantly poorer in this group than in those who had not been treated previously.

Although not enough cases were found who expressed disgust about sexuality to apply statistical tests, it appears that expressions of disgust about intercourse or about pelvic examination are a sign of poor prognosis.

Those patients who appeared to be primarily motivated by the wish for a baby rather than the wish to consummate *per se* had a significantly worse prognosis.

Although a high proportion of patients who made any comments about their husbands described them as kind and considerate, this was without prognostic significance.

Childhood sexual trauma does not appear to be an important cause of later non-consummation.

Those patients who experienced considerable pain during menstruation or otherwise connected it with suffering had a significantly worse prognosis.

The use of physical methods in treatment (beyond the performance of pelvic examination and self-examination, done in almost all cases) had no significant effect on outcome.

The seminar doctors believe that the prognosis is probably more favourable when the patient's relationship with her mother has been relatively good; this could not be evaluated from the material presented in the case reports.

Helping the patient to examine her fearful, unrealistic fantasies about intercourse is a central aspect of treatment. The prognosis was poorer in those cases showing a high degree of fantasy activity.

CHAPTER 9

Summary and Conclusions

Practising psychotherapeutic medicine requires a shift in attitude on the part of the doctor as well as the acquisition of new skills. The main trend of scientific medicine has been the study and treatment of diseases, at first conceived largely in anatomical terms, later in terms of disordered physiology and biochemistry. Less attention has been paid to the ill person. The shift in attitude required in the doctor before psychotherapy can take place involves his recognition that he is dealing with a whole human being who cannot be understood as a mere collection of organ systems. He must be aware both of the patient's uniqueness, in that no two lives are ever the same, and of those aspects of her way of experiencing life which are similar to those of other people.

In treating patients with sexual problems, such as nonconsummation, the doctor must become aware of far more than the sexual anatomy and physiology he learned in medical school, so that he can understand the problem in terms of the patient's emotional life—her feelings about her body and about the important people in her life. A large part of medical treatment consists of the doctor doing something to the patient, whose main responsibility is one of passively

141

allowing him to do it. In psychotherapy, the patient and doctor do something together; both are active participants. In a sense, their co-operative task—understanding some aspects of the patient's life in a new way—is more and more assumed by the patient herself; as psychotherapy proceeds, the patient does more and more of the work until she can do without the doctor's help completely.

The prototype of insight-directed psychotherapy is psychoanalysis. Psychiatrists have developed other techniques of psychotherapy directed towards increasing the patient's insight which differ in various respects from psycho-analysis. Training in psycho-analytic technique includes a personal psycho-analysis, and this is generally held to be desirable for those learning to practise other forms of psychotherapy based on psycho-analytic knowledge. For various reasons this background can rarely be acquired by non-psychiatric physicians, who must nevertheless cope somehow with the emotional difficulties presented by their patients. This book has been concerned with one method of brief psychotherapy using skills which can be acquired by doctors in the course of a case discussion seminar conducted by a psycho-analyst. These methods, which have been discussed in the context of work with virgin wives, have a broader application. Evidence has been presented to indicate that these skills are teachable, and are more effective in helping patients to consummate their marriages than are standard gynaecological techniques.

Integrating the physical examination with psychotherapy is an important aspect of this technique; in this respect it is similar to the methods described by Michel-Wolfromm (1953), although developed independently. In dealing with the problem of non-consummation, this combined technique is highly effective. Comparable results have been reported using psychotherapy alone (Abraham, 1956), but the psychotherapy was done by a highly trained psycho-analyst.

One defence commonly used by women who have not consummated their marriages to deal with conflicting emotions about sexuality is the defence of 'not knowing'; I have termed this the Sleeping Beauty syndrome. The attempt to 'teach the facts of life' to such a patient usually fails, since it takes no account of the defensive function such 'ignorance' serves. Interpretation of the defence, combined with encouraging the patient to examine her genitals, helps her to overcome her inhibition in knowing about her own sexuality. This has been discussed in Chapter 3, illustrated by the cases of Mrs. Able, Mrs. Willis, and Mrs. Randell. It is also an element in the cases of Mrs. Burton (Chapter 6) and Mrs. Owen (Chapter 7).

The fantasies a patient has about her body and about sexual intercourse are important determinants of her behaviour. Fantasies that intercourse is a painful or destructive act, ideas that their vaginas are too small, fears of pregnancy or delivery, and confusion between vagina and rectum are some of the fantasies expressed by patients in this series. Facile reassurance of the fearful patient is far less effective than helping the patient to talk about her fantasies and to examine her conflicting fears and wishes. The expression of fantasy material has been shown in most of the cases presented in detail, particularly the cases of Mrs. Randell (Chapter 3), Mrs. Parker (Chapter 7), and Mrs. Weiss (Chapter 7).

Many patients in this series were women whose open or covert aggressiveness interfered with their sexual lives; the legendary figure of Brunhild was used as a prototype for these traits. When the doctor could recognize and accept the aggressiveness in the patient's relationship with her husband (often re-enacted in her relationship with the doctor) and communicate this understanding to the patient in the form of meaningful interpretations, the patient could become freer

143

to behave differently. Chapter 4 was concerned with this theme, as illustrated in the cases of Mrs. Holmes, Mrs. Wilson, and Mrs. Davis; it also appeared in Chapter 5 in the case of Mrs. Clarke, in Mrs. Lowe's case (Chapter 6), and in Mrs. Owen's case (Chapter 7).

Some patients in the series requested artificial insemination so that they could have a baby without intercourse. Although this may occasionally represent a realistic solution to otherwise insurmountable difficulties, the doctor must help the patient to examine the fantasies which may lie behind this wish. Such requests may represent derivatives of primitive unconscious fantasies, far removed from adult sexuality. The husband-wife relationship may be overshadowed by the mother-child relationship in such cases, and powerfully rejective attitudes towards their husbands may be involved. Chapter 5 discussed the implications of this and the data in Chapter 8 showed the significance of similar factors in a larger proportion of cases where the wish for a baby was strong without a corresponding wish for intercourse.

Other gynaecological procedures sometimes advised, such as stretching the patient's vaginal orifice under anaesthesia or the use of dilators, are charged with fantasy-meaning for the patient. Here again the discussion of the emotional implications of the procedure helps the patient to deal with her unconscious conflicts in a more mature way. Several cases in Chapter 7 were presented to illustrate what the seminar doctors have learned about such fantasies.

Collusive patterns between husbands and wives became apparent in the course of this study. By and large the husbands of virgin wives appeared to be excessively forbearing and excessively accepting of their wives' disturbed behaviour. Their own anxieties about sexuality and aggressiveness were heightened by the conflict present in their wives. Just as neurotic symptom-formation can be viewed as the best available compromise between opposing tendencies within a single person the marital pathology—non-consummation—represents a compromise between the two partners, and both unwittingly collude to maintain it. A shift in the balance of forces within the wife can lead to resolution of the impasse without treatment of the husband in a large proportion of cases, even when the husband has been to some degree impotent. Whether similar results could be achieved by treating the husband alone remains a question for investigation. From the current study, it appears that in marriages which are unconsummated, the wife's attitude and behaviour have a substantial effect on the husband's potency. This was found to be true in many cases in the series, and is most dramatically illustrated in the case of Mrs. Able (Chapter 3).

In psychotherapeutic work, the doctor tries to maintain a detached but sympathetic attitude towards the patient's emotional difficulties, attempting to understand what the patient presents both from her point of view and from an objective viewpoint. In the technique described here, it has been a useful working principle for the doctor to consider any feelings he experiences during an interview as symptoms of the patient's illness. When the doctor feels something he should examine his feeling and try to understand it as an indication of something in the patient, rather than act upon the feeling. In her relationship with the doctor, the patient tends to duplicate patterns of previous relationships with her parents and with her husband. Chapter 6 was concerned with this topic, as illustrated in the cases of Mrs. Burton and Mrs. Lowe; Mrs. Holmes's case (Chapter 4) provided another example.

The brief technique described here differs in various respects from longer forms of psychotherapy. At times it has benefited the patient when the doctor departed from the traditional role of psychotherapeutic neutrality and behaved

145

in a more friendly or more angry manner towards the patient. More often than not, the doctor who acted on feelings rather than reflecting on them ended up playing a role which reduplicated an earlier situation in the patient's life, in a drama determined by the patient's conflicts. This was particularly likely to happen when some problem in the patient set off one of the automatic response patterns in the doctor. One of the training functions of the seminar was helping the doctor to become more aware of such collusive patterns which tended to retard the development of insight in the patient. The seminar doctors all emphasize how their flexibility has increased during their training as they learned something about their own blind spots from the comments of other doctors.

The method of interviewing used in this technique differs significantly from traditional medical 'history-taking'. Rather than seeking answers to specific questions, the doctor encourages the patient to speak freely. In this way emotional connections and fantasy content are elicited which would be stifled by the 'history-taking' approach. The doctor must be sensitive to what the patient communicates by her non-verbal behaviour as well—her tone of voice, facial expression, bodily movements, and manner of dress. He must learn to listen in a new way. When I questioned the doctors on what they felt they had learned from the seminar, all of them emphasized their greater understanding of how to listen to the patient. The doctor must hear more than the factual account contained in what the patient says. He must be alert to what is not being said. For example, the woman who talks a great deal about her mother and scarcely mentions her husband is, by omission, telling a great deal about her relationship with her husband. The extent to which the various people in the patient's life 'come alive' to the listening doctor provides valuable insight into the depth and qualities of her relationship with them.

146

As the patient talks, the doctor is also aware of what his experience has taught him are the emotions people commonly experience in the situation being described by the patient. For example, if the patient presents a picture of her mother as overbearing and controlling and at the same time speaks only of affectionate feelings for mother, the doctor suspects that the patient has idealized her mother in an attempt to keep out of awareness the angry feelings towards her which are probably also present. The patient who emphasizes how kind and considerate her husband is may be overcompensating for her guilt-laden wishes that he be much more forceful with her, or trying to make reparation for her guilty feeling that she has damaged him in some way.

When the doctor, as a result of his listening, understands something about the patient of which she is unaware, his task shifts to that of communicating his understanding to the patient in a form which will be useful to her, by making an interpretive comment. Skill in the timing and phrasing of interpretations must be developed, which involves an appreciation of how much insight the patient can tolerate at a given point in treatment. A detailed discussion of such matters of technique is beyond the scope of this book (see Balint & Balint, 1961).

Though the primary aim of the technique used by the F.P.A. doctors is to help the patient to consummate her marriage, some degree of improvement in a tense marital relationship generally occurs as well. Part of this is due to the broader repercussions in the marriage of the acceptance of sexual intercourse. The previous vicious circle of anxiety, hidden anger, and frustration is replaced by a benign circle of shared pleasure. While many unresolved problems often remain in other areas of the patient's living, the effects of the change that has taken place tend to be far-reaching.

This technique appears to be less useful with patients who

show only slight anxiety about the non-consummation. When successful character defences operate, largely eliminating conscious anxiety or depression at the expense of a constricted and emotionally impoverished life, long-term psychotherapy by a psychiatrist or psycho-analyst is indicated. The doctor working with this technique must recognize its limitations, so that he can refer patients whose problems are beyond his skill to a specialist for adequate treatment.

In reading the transcripts of the doctors' reports to the seminar I could distinguish three broad phases in their style. During the early months of the seminar, case presentations were generally brief and colourless. Material about the patient's life, her relationships, and the affective exchange during the interview was sparse. Facts were presented disconnected from their emotional context. When treatment was successful, the doctors seldom knew why.

During a long middle phase, cases were presented in much greater detail, with a richness of emotional content. A much clearer picture emerged of the patient's family and marital relationships and of the doctor-patient interaction. Discussions were animated and the doctor's technique was forcefully criticized. During this phase, recurrent patterns in different cases became clearer. With their growing understanding, the doctors became more confident in their work and could usually understand why treatment was successful when it was, although the failures were less readily explained.

The final phase was one of brief reports in which much was taken for granted as common knowledge in the group as a result of their growing experience. Little historical material was presented. When the doctor found a patient difficult to treat, she generally had some idea of the cause of this. Doctors experimented with imitating each other's styles with particular patients; some doctors who were naturally mild with patients tried to be more forceful in confronting a patient who reminded them of one who had responded well to treatment in the past by one of the more forceful doctors. Similarly, those doctors for whom forcefulness was natural were able to recognize patients who needed a milder approach, and tried to vary their technique accordingly. Thus in part the doctors learned by identifying with each other as well as with the group leader and found themselves somewhat changed in the process. Having discussed one hundred cases of non-consummation, the doctors felt sufficiently confident of their mastery of the techniques involved in treatment to shift their attention in seminar sessions to other types of problem, particularly those requiring more prolonged psychotherapy. They are justly proud of their technique for the treatment of virgin wives, which succeeds in more than 70 per cent of cases after a very few treatment sessions.

In a sense, psychotherapy is an inevitable part of all medical practice. Whatever else the doctor does, he also administers a dose of himself to the patient. This work is a further contribution to the study of the pharmacology of the drug 'doctor' (see Balint, 1957a). In this sense, the question is not whether the doctor does psychotherapy, but rather whether or not he does it skilfully, with conscious intent, with some idea of applicable techniques and probable results. The technique of psychotherapy described here, designed to help the patient with certain limited problems, is comparable to the minor surgery which is within the range of competence of the average doctor. In psychotherapy, as in surgery, the aphorism 'there is no minor surgery, only minor surgeons' is applicable; to perform a limited task well requires special skill, and well-intentioned but unskilful efforts can do more harm than good. The seminar method used in this work with doctors treating virgin wives is an effective means of developing the required skill in the doctor.

APPENDIX[1]

*Concerning a certain Lugne, a pilot, surnamed
Tudicla, who lived in the island of Rechru, and
whom his wife held in aversion because he was
very ugly.*

At another time, when the holy man was a guest in the island
of Rechru (Rathlin), a certain layman came to him and complained regarding his wife, who, as he said, had an aversion
to him, and would not allow him to enter into marital
relations. Hearing this, the saint bade the wife approach, and
began to chide her as well as he could on that account, saying:
'Why, woman, do you attempt to put from you your own
flesh? The Lord says, "Two shall be in one flesh". Therefore
the flesh of your husband is your own flesh.'

She replied 'I am ready to perform all things whatsoever
that you may enjoin on me, however burdensome: save one
thing, that you do not constrain me to sleep in one bed with
Lugne. I do not refuse to carry on the whole management of
the house; or if you command it, even to cross the sea, and
remain in some monastery of nuns.' Then the saint said:
'What you suggest cannot rightly be done. Since your husband

---

[1] From *Adomnan's Life of Columba*, edited by Andersen & Andersen,
London: Nelson, 1961, pp. 437 *et seq.* St. Columba was born in A.D. 521 in
Ireland and lived on Iona A.D. 563–597. Adomnan was 9th abbot of Iona, from
679 to 704, and was trained by the Abbot Cuimine who had himself been a
monk in St. Columba's time on Iona.

is still alive, you are bound by the law of the husband; for it is forbidden that that should be separated which God has lawfully joined.' After saying this, he continued: 'On this day let us three, myself, and the husband with his wife, pray to the Lord fasting.' Then she said: 'I know it will not be impossible that things appearing difficult or even impossible may be granted by God to you, when you ask for them.'

In short the wife agreed to fast on the same day, and the husband also with the saint. And on the night following, in sleep, the saint prayed for them. On the next day the saint thus addressed the wife, in the presence of her husband: 'Woman, are you today, as you said yesterday, ready to depart to a monastery of nuns?' She said: 'I know now that your prayer concerning me has been heard by God. For him whom I loathed yesterday I love today. In this past night, (how I do not know), my heart has been changed in me from hate to love.' Let us pass on. From that day until the day of her death, that wife's affections were indissolubly set in love of her husband; so that the dues of the marriage-bed, which she had formerly refused to grant, she never again denied.

BIBLIOGRAPHY

ABRAHAM, H. C. (1956). A contribution to the problem of female sexuality. *Int. J. Psycho-anal.* **37**, 351.

ARIETI, S. (ed.) (1959). *American handbook of psychiatry.* New York: Basic Books.

ARMOUR, M. (trans.) (1952). *The fall of the Nibelungs* (Das Nibelungenlied). London: Dent.

BALINT, M. (1954). Training general practitioners in psychotherapy. *Brit. med. J.* **1**, 115.

BALINT, M. (1955). The doctor, his patient, and the illness. *Lancet* **1**, 683.

BALINT, M. (1957a). *The doctor, his patient and the illness.* London: Pitman Medical; New York: International Universities Press.

BALINT, M. (1957b). Training medical students in psychotherapy. *Lancet* **2**, 1015.

BALINT, M. (1960). Training for psychosomatic medicine. *Adv. Psychosom. Med.* **1**, 167.

BALINT, M. & BALINT, E. (1961). *Psychotherapeutic techniques in medicine.* London: Tavistock Publications; Springfield, Ill.: C. C. Thomas.

BEASLEY, B. T. (1947). Dyspareunia. *South. M. J.* **40**, 646.

BERRY, A. N. (1952). The recognition and management of sexual maladjustment. *Amer. J. Obst.* **64**, 581.

BRERETON, G. (trans.) (1957). *The fairy tales of Charles Perrault.* Harmondsworth: Penguin Books.

CLAYE, A. M. (1955). The problem of dyspareunia. *N. Zealand med. J.* **54**, 297.

CURTIS, A. H. & HUFFMAN, J. W. (1950). *A textbook of gynecology* (6th ed.). Philadelphia & London: W. B. Saunders Co.

ELLERY, R. S. (1954). Frigidity and dyspareunia. *Med. J. Australia* **41**, 626.

EWALT, J. R., STRECKER, E. A. & EBAUGH, F. G. (1957). *Practical clinical psychiatry.* (8th ed.). New York: McGraw-Hill.

Bibliography

FAGAN, R. H. (1958). Management of the couple with the problem of unsuccessful intercourse. *West. J. Surg.* **66,** 302.

FRANK, R. T. (1948). Dyspareunia—a problem for the general practitioner. *J.A.M.A.* **136,** 361.

FREUD, S. (1949). *Collected papers* (Vol. IV). London: Hogarth Press.

GLIEBE, P. A. (1942). Dyspareunia. *West. J. Surg.* **50,** 43.

GRIFFITH, E. F. (1943) Treatment of sexual disorders in women. *Med. Press (Lond.)* **209,** 390.

HALL, S. P. (1952). Vaginismus as a cause of dyspareunia. *West. J. Surg.* **60,** 117.

HENDERSON, D. & GILLESPIE, R. D. (1956). *A text-book of psychiatry.* (8th ed.). London: Oxford University Press.

HILL, A. B. (1949). *Principles of medical statistics* (4th ed.). London: The Lancet Ltd.

JANNEY, J. C. (1950). *Medical gynecology.* (2nd ed.). Philadelphia and London: W. B. Saunders Co.

JEFFCOATE, T. N. A. (1957). *Principles of gynaecology.* London: Butterworth.

JOHNSTONE, R. W. (1944). Dyspareunia. *Practitioner* **152,** 142.

KEHRER, E. (1950). Uber Psycho-Gynäkologie. *Deutsche med. Wschr.* **75,** 110.

KEHRER, E. (1955). Die psychogenen gynäkologischen Krankheitsbilder und ihre Behandlung. *Münch. med. Wschr.* **97,** 1091.

KINSEY, A. C., POMEROY, W. B., MARTIN, C. E. & GEBHARD, P. H. (1953). *Sexual behavior in the human female.* Philadelphia and London: W. B. Saunders Co.

KROGER, W. S. & FREED, S. C. (1951). *Psychosomatic gynecology.* Philadelphia and London: W. B. Saunders Co.

LLOYD, O. (1950). Dyspareunia—investigation of causes and treatment. *Med. Press (Lond.)* **224,** 573.

MACLEOD, D. H. & READ, C. D. (1955). *Gynaecology* (5th ed.). London: Churchill.

MALLESON, J. (1942). Vaginismus—management and psychogenesis. *Brit. med. J.* **2,** 213.

MALLESON, J. (1952). Infertility due to coital difficulties: a simple treatment. *Practitioner* **169,** 161.

MALLESON, J. (1954). Sex problems in marriage with particular reference to coital discomfort and the unconsummated marriage. *Practitioner* **172,** 389.

MARSHALL, W. (1945). Overlooked factors in pathogenesis and treatment of dyspareunia. *Med. Times* (New York) **73,** 128.

MAYER, M. D. (1932). Classification and treatment of dyspareunia. *Amer. J. Obst.* **24,** 751.

MAYER-GROSS, W., SLATER, E. & ROTH, M. (1960). *Clinical psychiatry*. London: Cassell.

MEARS, E. (1958). Dyspareunia. *Brit. med. J.* **2**, 443.

MICHEL-WOLFROMM, H. (1953). Interférences du psychisme sur les troubles génitaux. *Semaine des Hôpitaux* **29**, 835.

MICHEL-WOLFROMM, H. (1954). Causes et traitement du vaginisme. *Rev. Fr. Gyn. Obst.* **49**, 30.

NOBÉCOURT, P. (1942). Une énigme de l'histoire: Pourquoi Louis XIII n'a-t-il pas consommé son mariage que trois années apres sa célébration? *Bull. Acad. Méd.* (Paris) **126**, 431.

NOVAK, E. & NOVAK, E. K. (1956). *Textbook of gynaecology*. (5th ed.). London: Bailière, Tindall & Cox.

NOYES, A. P. & KOLB, L. C. (1958). *Modern clinical psychiatry*. Philadelphia & London: W. B. Saunders Co.

PEEL, J. H. (1960). *Textbook of gynaecology* (5th ed.). London: Heinemann.

PERRAULT, C. *The fairy tales of Charles Perrault*, see Brereton.

PHILLIPS, J. (1940). The investigation and treatment of dyspareunia. *Clin. J.* **69**, 144.

REYMOND, J. C. (1951). La vie sexuelle de la femme. III. La dyspareunie. *J. Prat.* (Paris) **65**, 455.

RUBIN, I. C. & NOVAK, J. (1956). *Integrated gynecology* (3 vol.) New York: McGraw-Hill.

SMAIL, C. (1943). Vaginismus and dyspareunia: causes, management, and treatment. *Northwest Med.* **42**, 322.

VON MIKULICZ-RADECKI, F. (1948). Schwerigkeiten bei der Kohabitation. *Geburtshilfe und Frauenheilkunde* **8**, 409.

WALTHARD, M. (1909). Die Psychogene Aetiologie und die Psychotherapie des Vaginismus. *Münch. med. Wschr.* **56**, 1998.

WENGRAF, F. (1953). *Psychosomatic approach to gynecology and obstetrics*. Springfield, Illinois: Charles C. Thomas.

WHARTON, L. R. (1947). *Gynecology*. Philadelphia & London: W. B. Saunders Co.

INDEX